the
deepening
journey

To be out on the open water at sunset
facing backward, shore fading
like the past that I left behind,
we set our present course
into the beauty of the end of the day...
Our speed is slow and gentle enough
to allow my past to catch up to me
its drama unfolding as if it were yesterday-
and instead of looking away, I fixed my gaze there.
(For so long I have just wanted to leave it buried,
but the grave can't hold living things.)
Set in the midst of the beauty of the setting sun
and its safe embrace, a softness rises in me
laced with tears, washing my face, my soul
as I remembered the girl I left behind so long ago.
Left her standing there, hands full
of hunger, ache, resentment, shame, loneliness-
-hidden from all eyes, especially mine.
To forget her would heal me, I thought,
but the neglect of my own little soul was
just another arrow of abandonment,
piercing my present and my hunger.
But here, now, in this beauty I scoop her up
onto the seat next to me—wrapping my arms around her,
giving her the gift of her voice—her pain, her anger, her tears.
Feeling her youth and the shattering of her innocence.
Remembering how we had to survive by fortressing,
with grit and hardness—armoring up.
We were never thrown a life-line
as we tried to keep our head above water
as best we could.
Today, I pulled her out of those waters
into the lap of my soul and I mothered her.
Saw her. Held her. Held me.
Disarmed.

"Allowing My Past to Catch Up to Me"
Dana Andrechyn, July 2020

contents

welcome
and introduction

Welcome, friend!

We've been anticipating you … praying for you, hoping that you would join us on The Deepening Journey, as we explore more deeply our own stories, our truest self, God's heart for us, his Kingdom and our place in it, deepening our intimacy with God and with each other as we journey together!

There's a line in The Daily Prayer that we love, which says, "… take me DEEPER into Jesus today." We want to know the deep heart of God and to know his heart for us, his kindest intentions toward us. We want to mine the depths of who he is, and who he made each of us to be.

Is your heart longing for the opportunity to be still, to hear God and his wisdom for your life? Or, perhaps even more, to hear God's heart about your very existence? In our deepest hearts, we long to hear his voice respond to the questions of our hearts: Do you see me, Father? Does my heart matter to you? Am I pleasing to you? As a woman, what am I made for? Where do I fit in your design? Who did you create me to be?

Through The Deepening Journey video series and this journal workbook, we invite you into an exploration of these very questions with God. Whether you are just starting to become curious about this journey of deepening intimacy with God, or you have been on this exploration for years, we created this video series with you in mind. On your own or with friends, we pray you'll experience deeper intimacy with God, your own hearts, and together with your friends.

The Pulitzer Prize winning poet Mary Oliver wrote a poem called "The Journey." It inspires and invites us to experience a kind of knowing that reveals more of our true self.

The Journey

*One day you finally knew
what you had to do, and began,
though the voices around you
kept shouting
their bad advice–
though the whole house
began to tremble
and you felt the old tug
at your ankles.
"Mend my life!"
each voice cried.
But you didn't stop.
You knew what you had to do,
though the wind pried
with its stiff fingers
at the very foundations,
though their melancholy
was terrible.
It was already late
enough, and a wild night,*

*and the road full of fallen
branches and stones.
But little by little,
as you left their voices behind,
the stars began to burn
through the sheets of clouds,
and there was a new voice
which you slowly
recognized as your own,
that kept you company
as you strode deeper and deeper
into the world,
determined to do
the only thing you could do–
determined to save
the only life you could save.*

– Mary Oliver

Let's embark together on a journey that leads to a deeper knowing - a deeper experience of the life we were always meant to live and a discovering of who God had in mind for us to be when he thought about us, planned for us, and saw us even before he laid the foundations of the world. As we do this, it is our hope and desire that your intimacy with God and with friends will deepen as we walk together through The Deepening Journey!

With heart,

Robin   Sherry

All six video sessions can be accessed at **zoweh.org/tdj/watch**

how this works

How you choose to enter into *The Deepening Journey* is up to you. There are some important things to know beforehand. *The Deepening Journey* video series is designed to be experienced in the context of a weekly small group, a weekend retreat with your friends, or on your own. Watch each video session first, then engage that session's section in the journal workbook. If you are going stream the videos online, a good and reliable internet connection is needed.

Meet Your Guides

When embarking on a journey, it is always good to have guides with you who have made the journey before. To meet the team who will guide you through *The Deepening Journey*, please turn to page 111.

A Guide for Leaders

Coordinating a small group can be intimidating, whether this is your first time leading a group or you have been gathering and guiding women in a group setting for years. Download the Leader Guide at **TheDeepeningJourney.com.**

Conversation with Friends

Each session includes a segment with questions designed to invite you into deeper understanding through responding to what you've heard and listening to each other's experiences after watching the video. We encourage you to read the Guide to Extravagant Listening on pages 11-21 before beginning.

Time Alone With God

Each session includes a Time Alone With God segment for reflection and taking your questions to God. This is a significant practice to engage between gatherings, deepening your intimacy, oneness, and connectedness to God.

A Note About Film Clips

We use film clips through the series to facilitate conversation and critical thinking. Stories have a way of capturing our hearts and minds -- and we're often particularly drawn to stories of a world larger than our own: Wonderland, the Secret Garden, Narnia, Hogwarts, and more. These epic tales point us to the truth of the Kingdom. *Some film clips played during the recording of The Deepening Weekend did not make it into the final cut.* **All movie clips and trailers showing throughout The Deepening Journey are for educational purposes only.**

a guide to
extravagant listening

Amid your labors,
along your road,
may there be sisters
to tend you
and welcome you in.

Jan Richardson

Being able to tell our story, both the good and the bad, to someone who listens with compassion,
helps to develop new, healthy, and whole stories--regardless of what prior experiences a person
may have had. Telling stories that include both brokenness and blessing to a compassionate
other, leads to empathic understanding of others and ourselves and interrupts patterns of
intergenerational violence. When this includes the experience and knowledge of God's loving
presence within us and all around us, it can profoundly alter our sense of ourselves and our
relationship to creation at the deepest levels.

Richard Rohr

Oh, that we each might be that "compassionate other" referred to by Richard Rohr! May it be so as we share our hearts and stories with each other, caring well for the hearts of others in a circle of friends, as well as for your own heart on this journey!

We are living in an unprecedented time in our world. There has been so much change, so much pain, and so much loss. We are holding a lot. And we are also holding our own stories of harm, betrayal, and abuse. It is staggering. Is it any wonder we are crying out for help, for support, for comfort? We need someone to truly listen, to attune to us (attunement is about understanding another's inner emotional world. The window into another's emotional world is their nonverbal communication--that is, their facial expressions, tone of voice, and body language.), to hold space for us to share, and honor our story.

We need someone to bear witness to some of the weight we are carrying and join us in our grief. This is an opportunity for anyone who is given the honor of hearing another's story of struggle, wounding, and pain.

What if we are able to offer a safe and welcoming space for one who is hurting and courageous enough to share her story, to come alongside her, listen well as she shares? This is a sacred space. Holy ground.

We are wounded in isolation and thus we are mended in the setting of a healthy community. Healing is possible in the presence of safety, compassion, and good care. Isn't it incredible to know that this time together has the opportunity to be healing and to bring some level of freedom to a person as we bear witness to their story and their pain? What a privilege to join with another woman and with God in this way!

He uncovers deep things out of darkness, and brings the shadow of death to light.
Job 12:22

You are partnering with Trinity--Abba Father, Jesus, and Holy Spirit for your heart and the hearts of your friends through *The Deepening Journey*. You are not alone! Thank God! The Presence of God in you-- through your presence -- is how the Kingdom comes here on earth. This is the place where Love rises in you and through you. May it be so!

In Psalm 3:3 David cries out to God asking him to be a shield and a "lifter of my head." This lifting is the gift you can offer others. Essentially your way of being present says to them that you will not join the ranks of anyone that shames them for being too much or not enough or for being too out of step morally, and so on. You are there to lift their downcast eyes to a loving gaze that forgives and welcomes the weak and the wounded back home.

Brené Brown said, *"One of the most valuable gifts in my life was from my mom. She taught us to never look away from pain. The lesson was simple and clear:*
Don't look away. Don't look down. Don't pretend not to see hurt.
Look people in the eye.

Even when their pain is overwhelming. And when you're hurting and in pain, find people who can look you in the eye. We need to know we're not alone--especially when we're hurting."

Note: We ALL experience seasons of pain and suffering, and we experience seasons of being able to offer comfort and care. Both thread through our individual stories. Each season is part of our growth and maturity. In a sense, it helps to convey,

> *"You are right on time, and this is familiar to Jesus--He is well acquainted with grief."*

What an opportunity to see, hear, honor, and engage another, as women on the same path, in the middle of a journey, meeting in a sacred moment arranged for by God for his purposes in our lives!

Henri Nouwen speaks to this connective togetherness brilliantly and beautifully:

"When we honestly ask ourselves which person in our lives means the most to us, we often find that it is those who, instead of giving advice, solutions, or cures, have chosen rather to share our pain and touch our wounds with a warm and tender hand. The friend who can be silent with us in a moment of despair or confusion, who can stay with us in an hour of grief and bereavement, who can tolerate not knowing, not curing, not healing and face with us the reality of our powerlessness, that is a friend who cares."

Helpful Listening and Responding

> *The first duty of love is to listen.*
> *Paul Tillich*

Can you think of a time when someone sat with you face to face, leaned in, and listened intently as you shared with them a story of when you were hurt or betrayed or abandoned in some way? What was that like for you? What did it feel like? What did it invite in you?

Intentional, helpful listening is:
- Keeping my mind and heart open and curious.
- Holding the space for them and giving them my undivided attention.
- Being fully present. When we are fully present and engaged, we communicate, "You are important, and so are the things you are saying. I hear you. I see you. I care about you and your story. It matters."
- Engaging them - their whole person - with my whole person. Allowing them to affect me. i.e., to grieve with those who grieve.
- Offering them the dignity of being heard - having their story witnessed.

We each have different styles of relating, and yet there are ways we can be with another person that show care, honor, kindness, and compassion in ways that have the potential to bring/facilitate healing. There are also ways in which we can be unhelpful, causing someone to shut down, to experience deeper shame, and to be potentially more harmful.

Unhelpful Listening and Responding

Can you think of a time when you shared with someone who did not listen well? Perhaps they interrupted you, interjected their own story, or dismissed you in some way? Perhaps they diminished your pain by offering reasons or excuses or pat answers. What was that like for you? What did it feel like? What did it invite in you?

Answering before listening is both stupid and rude.

Proverbs 18:13

I recently shared with a small group of friends about a very painful encounter I had just had with my dad during our family's vacation at the beach. One friend asked, "When did that happen?"

I said, "It was Day-5 of our week."

She said with a nervous laugh, "Well, at least you had five good days!"

That comment was not only unhelpful, it was also very insensitive, unkind, so dismissive to my pain, and actually felt like more of the harm I had just endured from my dad.

Styles of Relational Care

Sometimes, despite our heart to offer care, we venture into some typical styles of engaging that are simply not helpful, and could even be harmful. Here are a few examples, adapted from The Allender Center's Story Sage material:

The Bulldozer offers insight into someone's response or story; but instead of moving with compassion and wisdom, Bulldozers go barging into painful territory as if they can just break and enter in without being invited. The sharer will likely feel afraid.

The Advice Giver avoids entering story, and instead tends to a person's heart by offering practical advice such as "read this book," or "take this class." There is certainly a time and place for offering helpful things, but this can often be a way of sidestepping care. The sharer will likely feel dismissed.

The Story Diverter/Co-Opter assumes her own story is the best guide to understanding someone else's, and co-opts the time by shifting attention to her own story as a means of offering help. It leaves the person who is sharing feeling burdened to offer care while also feeling frustrated and abandoned.

The Interrogator asks multiple questions, assuming they are easily answered or that the person hasn't considered them (often, questions like "why didn't you just do this or that?"). This refusal to enter the story heaps heavy burdens on an already burdened person.

The Empathetic Groaner offers a sincere but unhelpful response. Groaning at each turn but never fully engaging with a person in their story can communicate that a their story is just too big or makes assumptions that an empathic response is sufficient on its own.

The Poker Face offers very little response in both verbal and non-verbal communication, thus is essentially silent. This reaction often comes from a place of being unsure of what to do and not wanting to cause harm, but it leaves the person sharing alone, afraid, and likely ashamed.

If you catch yourself responding in one of the above ways, it's okay! Don't panic. You might slip in one of these as you learn how to listen and engage well. It's when there is repetition of any of those things that it becomes unhelpful and potentially harmful.

What if you listen ...

Without interrupting?
Without judgment or bias or my own agenda?
Without distractions (cell phones, etc.)?
Without problem solving or trying to fix it?
Without thinking of what you want to say next?
Without giving advice or answers?
Without saying, "Well at least ... "?

Examples of what <u>NOT</u> to do

One evening I was in a small group, and we were checking in with each other before we started discussing the book we were reading together. One of the women vulnerably shared that her teenage son was struggling with depression, and she feared he was suicidal. Through her tears, she shared that he had been increasingly distant in recent months, and that she was at a loss. She felt helpless and scared.

Without a pause, one of the women in the group (Momma #2) jumped in and said, "I know exactly how you feel!! That happened to our son! He ... we ... It was awful!"

The momentum and focus then shifted from the hurting momma to Momma #2 and her story. I sat stunned in my seat. I'm quite sure my mouth was hanging open. What happened next brought tears to my eyes. The brokenhearted momma said, "I am so sorry for your pain!"

Do you see what happened here? Momma #2 was trying to be kind. She was also likely uncomfortable with the discomfort and pain of the other momma. She was trying to relate - I imagine so that Momma #1 wouldn't feel alone in her pain, when actually - ironically - it did just that! I'm sure Momma #1 felt even more alone after sharing that day.

Momma #2 unknowingly hijacked Momma #1's pain and made it about herself, missing an opportunity to join her in her ache, and perhaps ask a question or two that might help her stay in the story, and care for her just by being with her in it. As soon as I could, I addressed Momma #1 and said something like, "Oh friend. How incredibly hard. This must feel so scary. Do you want to share more about how hard this is for you?"

Another way we often respond to someone's struggle or pain is to throw well-meaning (but very unhelpful) pearls of wisdom their way. I witnessed a man share his ache over feeling abandoned by dear friends in the midst of a significant loss. Another man responded, "Remember, God never wastes our pain." I watched the hurting man zip up what he was feeling and "get it together" and he responded, "Oh yes. Thank you. That's right." It was a missed opportunity to care for him and perhaps explore his pain with him further.

Often in these moments we throw Scripture at those who are hurting. Or we offer, "I'll pray for you," and we move on to the next thing. This shuts the conversation down. It closes the door on an opportunity to join them where they are and engage them in a way that can actually offer some healing balm. When we offer verses or cliches initially, we may be attempting to help or to make things "better", when actually, we are often trying to make ourselves feel better, as we are often very uncomfortable with others' emotions, struggle, and pain. We want to rescue, when what they are really crying out for is for their struggle and pain to be witnessed and joined with.

Author and speaker Brené Brown calls this empathy and illustrates it beautifully in an animated video describing empathy. In her video, she points out the four qualities of empathy:

1. Perspective taking - the ability to take the perspective of another person
2. Recognizing their perspective is their truth
3. Staying out of judgment
4. Recognizing emotion in another person, then communicating that.

This illustrates how empathy fuels connection. It is feeling WITH people. Empathy is a vulnerable choice. In order to connect with you, I have to connect with something in myself that knows that feeling.

Sometimes we don't know how to respond, and that's okay! Often, what might feel most helpful for the one sharing is for you to simply say, "I don't even know what to say. I'm just so glad you told me."

It is an honor to bear witness to another woman's story through her responses - especially those of pain, sorrow, and heartache. To hold space for their story, their pain - to bear their burden with them, if only for a few moments, can be an incredible gift.

Part of bearing witness is acknowledging what they have shared, while being aware of when you catch yourself wanting to respond with something comforting - "it's going to be okay"- simply because you are uncomfortable! What if instead, the most comforting response is to take a breath, and say, "That sounds so hard (weighty, painful, uncomfortable). Thank you for sharing with me."

Asking Meaningful Questions

If there is any confusion or doubt about what you are hearing (especially if you sense that it's important), good questions can help her clarify. Ask her if you may repeat what you think you heard, so that she can confirm that you heard correctly. Try to "mirror" what she said. Use her exact words, if you can. This kind of active listening is valuable. Learning how to ask good questions is paramount to listening well. Here are a few guidelines:

- Good questions invite thoughtful responses, stories, and opportunities to express how the person is feeling.
- Questions should be thoughtful, short, respectful, pertinent, and open-ended (open-ended questions cannot be answered with a simple 'Yes' or 'No').
- Avoid leading or judgmental questions, judgmental questions, and questions that suggest a solution.

- Questions should not be shot off rapid fire. Give her time to dwell on and explore one question before asking another, listening well to her responses.
- Remember to be curious!

Examples of Good Questions

Some questions we've found helpful to ask so that a friend may feel heard, seen, and known, include:

- Tell me more about that? What else?
- Can you put words to the tears that are starting to come?
- I wonder if you allow yourself to be angry at what was done to you? I feel angry with you...on your behalf.
- Do you want to say more about that? (about the anxiety, the rejection, the betrayal)
- How are you making sense of that?
- What do you do with the hurt? It's so hard to contend with the hurt.
- How are you feeling in your body right now?
- Where are you finding God in your story? (I wait until toward the end of her sharing to ask this, as sometimes this can tend to move us away from the story and the important details and emotions that need to be engaged, until they are ready to move on.)

Please walk with Jesus in the moment here...asking the Spirit "What is needed now?" Silence? Several deep breaths? Another clarifying question?

Jesus is our ultimate example. He asked over 300 questions in the gospels. Questions like:

- What do you want?
- Why are you afraid?
- Do you believe that I am able to do this?
- Will you wait with me?

Silence is Golden

How do you feel when there is silence in a conversation? Does it make you uncomfortable? Do you feel a need to fill it with words and conversation? This might be something to be curious about.

Pay attention to moments when you might be feeling the need to say something because the silence feels awkward, and you want to rescue the woman sharing (and yourself!). She may need a few minutes of silence to process her thoughts and feelings. She may not be used to truly being listened to, and it might take her some time to adjust to it. Ask if it is okay for you to take notes so that you can listen more thoroughly and be attuned to what the Holy Spirit is stirring in you.

What if we learn to be okay with silence?

We aim to be attuned to the Spirit in each moment, knowing what is needed and what is not.

What we are hopeful you'll experience in your conversations

As you meet with friends throughout the six weeks of The Deepening Journey, after each video session, you'll have conversations around the content, sharing how your hearts each respond to what you've heard, offering the stories of your lives in these responses. We are hopeful that as you learn and practice listening, each woman will experience feeling heard, seen, and known, as you each:

Fully engage with each woman's response. This means letting your heart get close to the heart and story of whomever is sharing with you. Let it affect you. Let emotions and empathy come. Allow yourself to be sad and angry and fearful with them. We know this is not the end of the story, but we need to be with them in the pain and get close to it and find them in it. To do this, we must pay attention to their words, their body language, what our own bodies and souls are picking up on by being with them -- all of this because we are fully tuned in to the person in front of us, the events of their story, and the affect that it left on their being. For example, *I hear you saying how terrified you were when this event took place. I feel that with you. I see it in your eyes and am so thankful for your tears. I feel deeply sad in my chest and my stomach is in knots. I hate that this happened, it absolutely should not have happened.*

Be a safe space. When someone is willing to share her deep anxieties, fears, and struggles, you are entering a holy space. This is sacred ground. It's time to take your shoes off, figuratively speaking. Honor her courage as she may be in her most vulnerable state. The way you handle her heart matters. We are not asking or expecting you to heal or fix her life … as if this is possible! We know this is unkind and unfair to expect, and it is also impossible to "fix" someone and, thankfully, that is not the goal.

The goal is connection in a space of safety. You are simply holding space for each other to exhale, to be witnessed in their brokenness and beauty, and to invite Jesus to come. For example, *"Thank you for sharing this. I will not tell anyone else what you have shared. Whatever you are feeling is welcome and okay. In this moment you are safe. You can continue sharing, we can sit in silence together, you can cry."*

Believe for goodness to come on their behalf. When we tell our stories of pain it allows for a rewiring of our physical brains. Oftentimes after a wounding event, if our hearts are not tended to well and we do not get the care that we need, the pain gets stuck. When we listen and bear the weight of another and join them in their suffering, when we give space to let them come and share their burdens, there is the opportunity to allow the pain to lose a bit of its traumatic weight. This comes as they feel safe, that you are connected to them, and believe that God has healing, goodness, and Life available to them, without bright-siding or silver-lining their grief.

Feelings Matter

Feelings and emotions are a part of our humanity and play a crucial role in our healing. There is a common practice in the church at large to suggest that if we just bring our feelings under submission to God, or claim a particular passage of Scripture, all should be well. (For instance, has anyone ever quoted Jeremiah 29:11 or Romans 8:28 to you when you're just having a really awful day?) That practice is contrary to how God treats the issue of feelings. Scripture tells us that He keeps our tears in a bottle (Psalm 56:8). In other words, the Father treats our tears (our feelings) as precious things and honors them by making a memorial to them. If feelings were simply to be wrangled into submission, God would smash that bottle into oblivion rather than keeping it as a treasure.

Considering this, what if instead of shrinking back from our feelings, we choose to pour out our hearts, to actually experience the full range of feelings and emotions that we were created to experience with God? What if we invite and allow God to hold us in our pain, to speak to our hearts in the confusion and isolation, that He may lay a path back to life again for us? Sounds like the healing balm for which our souls yearn, a taste of the goodness of God in the land of the living. And this is also what we hope to offer others, even as we receive it ourselves.

Perhaps you, and the women you gather with for *The Deepening Journey*, have never had their experiences or their feelings honored. They may have been dismissed, been told to be brave, be forgiving, be forward looking. But to be those things, we need our pain to be cared for. We need someone to make a space for us to process what has happened. Feelings provide great opportunities to invite others (and ourselves) into exploration. To ask, "what is your (sadness, tears, anger, fear, hopelessness, etc.) about?" serves to open the door for deeper understanding of what you've experienced in a wounding or traumatic situation. Making that space for another person's heart requires that we have first made space for our own hearts. It is difficult to value the feelings and experiences of another when we don't value these for ourselves.

Important Reminders

As we offer this way of listening for you to consider as you gather with friends for *The Deepening Journey,* we want to remind you of the importance of remembering:

Confidentiality is critical (Proverbs 11:13). You have been entrusted with sacred stories of your friends. Please guard them.

How freeing to know that we are not doing this alone. We are partnering with the Living God who will anoint us as we surrender to Him and partner with Him. Your presence, Lord, is what we so desperately need.

God's timing is not our timing. Each woman may be taking her first step on a healing journey. As Larry Crabb said, "God is real. He is up to something good. It will take some time."

A core Zoweh tenet is the redeemed heart is good (Ezekiel 36:26). When appropriate, affirm that her heart is good, and that she is seen, known, and dearly loved.

We are always amazed how the Spirit of God seems to gather just the right women together! And we are often surprised by what God has in store for us as we listen to the responses, stories, and hearts of another. We witness the Spirit of God moving, softening, opening, revealing, speaking, and healing. It is such a beautiful and glorious thing to experience and witness.

After each session, perhaps pause, reflect, consider. Be curious about what comes up for you in your time with your friends. Where were you drawn in? What did your heart most connect with or move away from? What was your body feeling or wanting to do? All of this is connected to your own story, and we bring our story with us every time we relate to someone else.

prayer of dedication

Holy Trinity: Father, Son, and Spirit,

We rejoice in all that you are doing and will do in and surrounding The Deepening Journey. We praise your name and give you glory and honor for who you are. You are glorious. We stand together now in the name of Jesus to dedicate and consecrate this exploration through The Deepening Journey, bringing it all under the Kingdom of Christ. We bring the Kingdom of God and the work of Christ over the facilitators, each woman, over her life and her family. We ask you to fill the facilitators and all those engaged with The Deepening Journey with your Spirit, your strength, your love, and your glory. Let your Kingdom come now and fill this exploration through The Deepening Journey in every way.

God, we bring the fullness of the Cross, the Resurrection Life, and the power and authority of the Ascension of Jesus Christ against the kingdom of darkness and all that is set against our hearts in The Deepening Journey. By and through the great work of Jesus on our behalf, we cut off all foul spirits, foul powers and foul devices, and all evil set against our hearts, The Deepening Journey, and the orientation and freedom that is at hand. We bind Satan, all his emissaries, and all their work set against every woman stepping into this exploration and work of heart in the name and authority of Jesus Christ.

Holy Spirit, we invite you to prepare each heart. Open our hearts and minds, and arrange for the receiving of your guiding, teaching, provoking, and invitation to more. Holy Spirit, open the deep places within us, fill us with your love, and remind us of your love for us. Strengthen us, Holy Spirit, to receive all that you have for us in and through this exploration of our hearts. Spirit of God, we pray for an unveiling of anything that stands in the way of our receiving your love. Reveal to us the messages we have received along our journey. We invite you to reveal any false beliefs we are holding about our hearts and your heart toward us.

Jesus, we ask for healing. We declare that we need healing! Jesus, reveal to us the places in our stories where we have been wounded, hurt, betrayed, and shamed, and show us the effect of those wounding moments and the messages. Reveal to us the lies they might have inflicted and that we carry even today.

We bring the Kingdom of God and the full work of the Lord Jesus Christ against the warfare coming against our life. We proclaim our citizenship is in heaven and that the Kingdom of God is an everlasting kingdom, and that we belong to God. In the powerful name of Christ, we claim the love and protection of His Kingdom against any and all forces opposed to our life and our freedom in the Larger Story. We extend this prayer of protection over Zoweh, The Deepening Journey Guide Team, and all those involved in the making and financing of this resource.

Father, we pray against and prohibit the enemy's attempts to compromise the mission of our hearts' healing and wholeness. We declare and proclaim that greater is He who is in us than he that is in the world - and because of this truth, we now claim the victory in the spiritual battle for our hearts and we claim the turning of the tide in the battle for each woman who is a part of The Deepening Journey, now and to come!

In the name of the Lord Jesus, we forbid all foul spirits that will attempt to work against us: shame, guilt, fear, diminishment, depression, discouragement, anger, anxiety, accusation. Father, we invite your canopy of love and protection over this journey in every way.

Trinity God, we rejoice in all that you have done, are doing, and all that you are about to do in the hearts and lives of all those associated with The Deepening Journey. Come in glory. Come in tenderness. Come in power and authority. We stand together to declare your glory and greatness over The Deepening Journey, and over all those bringing it.

Come in your fullness, God. We proclaim Love and Life, Healing and Freedom over our hearts and our exploration of The Deepening Journey. We call on your blessing and your provision for this mission, with each successive session. We worship you. We are so grateful to be launching this grand endeavor to restore our union with you, to affirm our hearts, and to guide us and direct us to new places of Life and Love.

We pray and proclaim all of this in the matchless name of our Lord Jesus Christ, our Savior, our Shepherd, and our King!

Amen and AMEN!

once upon a time ...

Those who have a strong sense of love and belonging have the courage to be imperfect.

Brené Brown

Deep in the recesses of our minds and hearts there lies hidden the treasure we seek. We know its preciousness, and we know that it holds the gift we most desire: a life stronger than death.

Henri Nouwen

In this session, we consider the story in which we find ourselves, and the core truth that women were made to experience belovedness, wholeheartedness, and to bring the image of God to bear through strength, beauty, relationships, and the Mother heart of God.

Three Foundational Truths about Women

We were created for Love (belovedness).

We were created for Shalom (wholeheartedness).

We were created in God's Image (image bearers).

Being the Beloved

> *In all of our hearts lies a longing for a Sacred Romance. It is set deeply within us ... and will not go away. It is the core of our spiritual journey. It draws us toward home. Any religion that ignores it survives only as guilt-induced legalism; a set of propositions to be memorized and rules to be obeyed.*
>
> — Brent Curtis and John Eldrege,
> *The Sacred Romance*

How does God being described as "the Ageless Romancer" land on your heart? Women long to be seen and known - fully - for who we really are and LOVED just exactly as we are. We were created to be regarded with affection, delight ... to be enjoyed!

> *Beginning with the first day of life outside the womb, one of the core questions every child is asking is, "Am I loved?" This question marks us throughout life, and the answers we receive set the course for how we live.*
>
> — Dan Allender

Where Love is, God is. and Where God is, Love is.

- 1 John 4:8

We are the beloved of God. You are not what you do, although you do a lot. You are not what you have collected in terms of friendships and connections, although you might have many. You are not the popularity that you have received. You are not the success of your work. You are not what people say about you, whether they speak well or whether they speak poorly about you. All these things that keep you quite busy, quite occupied, and often quite preoccupied are not telling the truth about who you are. I am here to remind you in the name of God that you are the Beloved Daughters and Sons of God, and that God says to you, "I have called you from all eternity and you are engraved from all eternity in the palms of my hands. You are mine. You belong to me, and I love you with an everlasting love."

- Henri Nouwen

Women are the Beloved of God. Being loved - belovedness - is foundational for our deepening journey.

Being Wholehearted

Shalom is wholeness, fullness, wellness, completeness, peace, safety, and resting secure. We were created for and meant to experience intimacy, union, flourishing, belovedness, delight, safety, freedom, goodness, and play with God in the Garden of Eden.

This is who we were before the world, parents, teachers, coaches, relatives, told us otherwise. In other words, this is a picture of our **True Self.**

The Shalom we were meant to experience is about delight and honor: delight for God, delight for his creation, delight for engagement with one another, but also delight for who you are! You are stunningly created and crafted. You were made for someone to see you and to be captured by you!

You are the most remarkable spirit I have ever met. You have courage and resourcefulness, talent, you're proud - wonderfully so! And you are cunning and vibrant ... completely alive! You deserve every happiness you find. What I mean is ... you deserve much more! You deserve magic. - Tolkien, 2019 film

Consider ...

How easy is it for you to receive a compliment or encouragement? Honor and delight? Consider Psalm 139:17, do you actually believe God has precious thoughts about you? And if he does, do you have a hint as to how he sees you to be precious? And what would it be like to actually hold that, to experience, and taste that?!

You were meant for LOVE - you are the Beloved. You were meant for the receiving and giving of delight and honor. You bear delight and honor as you bear the very image of God!

Your thoughts about me, O God,
are precious.

- Psalm 139:17

Being Image Bearers

God spoke: "Let us make human
beings in our image, make them
reflecting our nature" ... He created
them male and female.

- Genesis 1:27-28

God created man alone and said it wasn't good until there was woman. In order to fully represent and reflect their nature, the Trinity needed **both** masculine **and** feminine. God is neither male nor female. Both genders together are needed to reflect the image of the Trinity.

Four of the many unique ways we bear the image of God as women:

1. through Strength
2. through Beauty
3. in Relationships
4. through the Mother Heart of God

Women Bear the Image of God through Strength

In *Wonder Woman,* watch to see how Diana has a settled strength that is rooted and grounded in LOVE. Everything she does comes from a place of love. It's what motivates her.

At our deepest level, we have within
us Trinity DNA. We are triune beings -
body, soul, spirit. Made in the image of
a Triune God.

- Michael Thompson

The strength of a woman is beautiful, powerful, and needed to partner with God - to act on behalf of those who are bound and not yet free, those who are oppressed, those whose voices have been silenced.

> *He has sent me to proclaim freedom for the prisoners, recovery of sight for the blind, to set the oppressed free and to proclaim the year of the Lord's favor.*
>
> **- Luke 4:18-19**

We bring our strength in the power and authority of the Lord Jesus Christ against Satan and his kingdom - the evil that opposes them.

> *The Lord God said, "It is not good for the man to be alone. I will make a helper suitable for him."* **- Genesis 2:18**

The Hebrew word for "helper" is *Ezer kenegdo,* which literally translates to **warrior; strong help; man's perfect match.**

When we think of it in relationship with men, it is the picture of two parts of equal weight leaning against one another.

This powerful Hebrew word – Ezer - points to a woman's calling to combat evil and the powers of the kingdom of darkness and where we see this in our world - and on behalf of others! **To use our strength, our voice, our presence, our beautifully fierce heart to protect, to act justly - on behalf of those who are weak, unprotected, oppressed, violated, abused, trafficked, poor, and marginalized.**

> *He has shown you, O mortal, what is good. And what does the Lord require of you? To act justly and to love mercy and to walk humbly with your God.*
>
> **- Micah 6:8**

Real strength never impairs beauty or harmony, but it often bestows it, and in everything imposingly beautiful, strength has much to do with the magic.

- Herman Melville

Women Bear the Image of God through Beauty

For we are God's masterpiece. He has created us in Christ Jesus ...

- Ephesians 2:10

We are God's masterpiece!

Women are the crown of creation. It is about far more than outward appearance. Beauty is something that is set in our hearts. A woman's beauty is the very life of God within her.

Consider ...

Consider the beauty of a comforting touch, a warm embrace, the beauty of tears of empathy, eyes that welcome and invite, the beauty of an encouraging smile, the beautiful sound of a laugh, the beauty of a settled heart, the beauty of someone's presence. Think of a time you've experienced this ... and a time when you've offered this.

Our very presence can bring goodness, life, and healing to another. Beauty captivates. It awakens us. It draws us in. It engages our senses and delights and nourishes us!

We have an enemy that despises the beauty we bring to bear in this world. He will attempt to mar it in countless ways.

> **There's always a sunrise and always a sunset and it's up to you to choose to be there for it, "Put yourself in the way of beauty."** - Cheryl Strayed, *Wild: From Lost to Found on the Pacific Crest Trail*

Create beauty. Add beauty. Give yourself beauty. Enjoy beauty. Offer beauty.

Women Bear the Image of God in our capacity for Relationships

One of the most beautiful (and brilliant and powerful) ways women bear the image of our God is through our capacity for relationships. Women are deeply relational, made in the image of a deeply relational Trinity God!

> **The story that is the Sacred Romance begins ... with God in relationship, intimacy beyond our wildest imagination, heroic intimacy. The Trinity is at the center of the universe; perfect relationship is the heart of all reality. Think of your best moments of love or friendship or creative partnership, the best times with family or friends around the dinner table, your richest conversations, the acts of simple kindness that sometimes seem like the only things that make life worth living.**
>
> - Brent Curtis and John Eldredge,
> *The Sacred Romance*

RELATIONSHIPS are LIFE.

A deep sense of love and belonging is an irreducible need of all women, men, and children. We are biologically, cognitively, physically, and spiritually wired to love, to be loved, and to belong. When those needs are not met, we don't function as we were meant to. We break. We fall apart. We numb. We ache. We hurt others. We get sick. There are certainly other causes of illness, numbing, and hurt, but the absence of love and belonging will always lead to suffering.

- Brené Brown, *The Gifts of Imperfection*

There is something in us that longs to be wanted, to be invited, to be included. Belonging - connection - happens in the context of relationships. It's what we long for, because we were made for it!

Women Uniquely Reflect and Bring the Mother Heart of God to Bear in the World

---

Consider ...

Consider beyond the biological sense what it means 'to mother': give birth to, produce, bear, bring forth, nurture, raise, protect, tend, nurse, rear, care for, cherish. Women mother in so many beautiful and brilliant ways! Who has mothered you? Who have you mothered?

God is revealed in Scripture not only as a father but also as a mother.

How often I have longed to gather your children together, as a hen gathers her chicks under her wings, and you were not willing.

- Jesus, Matthew 23:37

33

He longs to show us affection, to comfort us when we suffer and grieve, to care for us, and tend to our wounds. To me this sounds like the heart of a kind and nurturing mother! We bear the image of God when we protect, provide, comfort, and care.

We mother by nurturing. The word *nurture* shares the same root word as nurse.

El Shaddai means "the strong-breasted One." *El Shaddai* describes the Mother Heart of God, who longs to embrace, nurture, and nourish us.

We believe this is just some of what was in the heart of God when He made woman. We were made to be loved and to love, to experience *Shalom* - wholeheartedness - to bear God's image in Strength, Beauty, Relationships, and Mothering.

Conversation with Friends ...

As a group, take turns sharing your responses to the video and these questions.

1. What was your experience of being seen and known as a child? When and where did you feel safe, wanted, valued, and held?

2. In what ways did you experience care as a young girl?

3. Which of these ways that women bear the Image of God is the most difficult for you to identify with?

    i. Strength

    ii. Beauty

    iii. Relationships

    iv. The Mother Heart of God

Time Alone with God

Before the next gathering, carve out time to be still. Find a quiet place, and bring the questions of your heart to God.

1. Father, how did you see me as a young girl? In what ways did you know me, value me, and hold me close? How do you see me now? Are your thoughts about me really precious?

2. Jesus, where have I known and felt the absence of love and belonging?

3. Holy Spirit, what are the ways that you mother me and care for me? What things are in the way of receiving your love? Where do I push back against your care?

Stories from the Journey: Lenné Responds

When men talk with other men, and they're getting to know one another, probably the most common question they ask is, "What do you do for a living?" But for women, it's a different question. What we often ask is, "Do you have children?" That's a hard question for me. I had two miscarriages in my early 30's and never got pregnant again after that. So when I sense the question coming, I grit my teeth and say as positively as I can, "No, I don't have children; I have dogs."

The clear truth is that dogs are not substitutes for children - not even close - and my soul knows that very well. So this issue of kids is one of the things that makes me feel different in the company of women. The statistics say that about 85% of women will have children, so I'm part of a very small club that I don't really want membership in.

People often don't know what to say when I tell them I don't have children. Wanting to be kind, they usually respond with something like, "Oh, we can mother in other ways." That thought always struck me as some lame consolation prize. But I feel differently about that now.

The Mother Heart of God is so much bigger than we have known. Think back to what Robin said in the video about God as El Shaddai, the strong-breasted one. Consider the literalness of that. What is God saying about himself? You have to start with what breasts do. They provide nourishment that keeps children alive and enables them to grow. Then there's also the aspect of nursing that involves holding children against your breast and the warmth, safety, and protection of that - of being held close.

Consider the verb "to mother." It involves nurture - the care of the whole person - body, soul, and spirit. Developing them, training, and encouraging them. Here is how that's been applied in my life. In the course of growing up, the vast majority of the world, even Christians, have acquired an orphan spirit. This is true no matter how good their parents have been. Inevitably, parents fall down and it creates injury to our hearts and produces questions about our worth and value. The orphan spirit is the driving force behind so much of how we wound others and our troubles in relationships. The antidote is nurture and safety, warmth and protection, and nourishment.

In the movie *Wonder Woman*, Diana says, "I used to want to save the world." The really great news is, we can save the world by offering what God offers through us, by tending to other's hearts, by seeing them and being safe places for them. By living protectively over them. And this is the Trinity's redemptive offer to me - that I can walk in the mother heart of God in this way. It is a deeply fulfilling thing for me, this tending to other's hearts and helping them feel safe and seen, loved and valued.

In my life as a psychologist, and now as a coach, I have had so many clients who would not have needed to see me if someone had loved them well. But that didn't happen. We can step in and do that. I'd ask you to consider what that looks like for you. And consider how you can offer it to the people God has placed you among. You have been placed here in this timeline, in this season, for these people, because your story is powerful. El Shaddai through you is powerful.

Extra Notes - Session 1

_____

_____

_____

_____

_____

_____

_____

_____

_____

_____

_____

_____

_____

_____

_____

_____

_____

_____

_____

_____

_____

Going Deeper ...

There is so much more to discover and consider in your journey, exploration, and increasing awareness of what God had in mind when he created you. Resources that we've found significant in our journey:

Being Known Podcast with Curt Thompson, MD

Becoming Myself, by Staci Eldredge

the false self: who we aren't

If I had told him the truth long ago, or had danced and drunk and sung more, maybe he would have seen me instead of a dependable, ordinary mother. He loves a version of me that is incomplete. I always thought it was what I wanted, to be loved and admired. Now I think perhaps, I'd like to be known.

Kristin Hannah, *The Nightingale*

*I want to unfold.
Let no place in me hold itself closed,
for where I am closed, I am false.
I want to stay clear in your sight.*

Rainer Maria Rilke, *The Book of Hours*

In this session, we begin to uncover the False Self we've created in order to protect ourselves and to secure love, and how, in response to shame, we attempt to hide, prove, or fear, causing the True Self to live small ... or larger than life ... or lost. The truth is, to discover who we are, we need to see who we aren't.

What is in the way?

What keeps us from the intimacy and flourishing that God intended for us?

> *A deep sense of love and belonging is an irreducible need of all people. We are biologically, cognitively, physically, and spiritually wired to love, to be loved, and to belong. When those needs are not met, we don't function as we were meant to. We break. We fall apart. We numb. We ache. We hurt others. We get sick.*
>
> **- Brené Brown**

We hide, creating a way of being and moving through the world in order to secure love, in order to belong, in order to find our place and fit in. In creating this False Self, we sacrifice our heart for the sake of not feeling unloved.

> *God looked over everything he had made; it was so good, so very good!*
>
> **- Genesis 1:31**

In Genesis 2, God tells us the story of creating man and woman in his image, blessing them, and giving them a lush garden in which to flourish. It was good - God even said it was 'very good.' He created us to live intimately with Him, to walk with Him, experience his love, goodness; to know Him.

The serpent was clever, more clever than any wild animal God had made. He spoke to the Woman: "Do I understand that God told you not to eat from any tree in the garden?" The Woman said to the serpent, "Not at all. We can eat from the trees in the garden. It's only about the tree in the middle of the garden that God said, 'Don't eat from it; don't even touch it or you'll die.'

The serpent told the Woman, "You won't die. God knows that the moment you eat from that tree, you'll see what's really going on. You'll be just like God, knowing everything, ranging all the way from good to evil."

When the Woman saw that the tree looked like good eating and realized what she would get out of it—she'd know everything!—she took and ate the fruit and then gave some to her husband, and he ate. Immediately the two of them did "see what's really going on"—saw themselves naked! They sewed fig leaves together as makeshift clothes for themselves.

When they heard the sound of God strolling in the garden in the evening breeze, the Man and his Wife hid in the trees of the garden, hid from God.

- Genesis 3:1-8

Consider ...

The enemy lured Eve into doubting and misinterpreting God's words and desires for her. Instead of rooting herself in belovedness, she was filled with doubt about God. You might even say Satan lured her into believing God was 'holding out on her.' Have you ever felt like God is holding out on you? When?

Satan is sinister, plotting, and strategic. He will do whatever it takes for you to believe lies about God, about yourself, about others, and about your life.

Consider ...

We hide, covering ourselves with fig leaves of the False Self. What do you do when you're feeling ashamed? Ashamed of what you've done, afraid of not being enough, afraid of not being seen, known, and loved? What is it that you cover with fig leaves? What are your go-to fig leaves?

There's a pretty good chance we've misinterpreted a situation or two or a hundred, believing lies about ourselves, about God, and about people around us. And those lies, my friends, are rocket fuel for the False Self.

Consider ...

Do you think Adam and Eve interpreted their lives and situation accurately? What do you think are the odds that you have interpreted your life accurately?

What is the True Self?

The True Self - a sense of self based on a spontaneous and authentic experience and a feeling of being truly alive. This is who God created you to be and how you bear His image. The True Self draws life and way and breath from God and is in alignment with God, she lives from her identity as a Beloved Daughter, and flourishes wholeheartedly in a full and abundant Kingdom Life.

What is the False Self?

The False Self - a defensive façade lacking spontaneity and leaving one feeling dead and empty – only having the mere appearance of being real. Also known as the Flesh.

The False Self is often aligned with the kingdom of darkness and can often make casualties or victims out of others and absolutely will make a casualty or victim out of its host, causing the true woman to live small or lost.

Afraid that our inner light will be extinguished, or our inner darkness exposed, we hide our true identities from each other. In the process, we become separated from our own souls. We end up living divided lives, so far removed from the truth we hold within that we cannot know the "integrity that comes from being what you are."

I yearn to be whole, but dividedness often seems the easier choice. A "still, small voice" speaks the truth about me, my work, or the world. I hear it and yet act as if I did not. I withhold a personal gift that might serve a good end or commit myself to a project that I do not really believe in. I keep silent on an issue I should address or actively break faith with one of my own convictions. I deny my inner darkness, giving it more power over me ... - Parker Palmer, *A Hidden Wholeness*

I don't really understand myself, for I want to do what is right, but I don't do it. Instead, I do what I hate. I want to do what is right, but I can't. I want to do what is good, but I don't. I don't want to do what is wrong, but I do it anyway.

- Romans 7:15, 18-19

This False Self is a strategy or "way" that each of us developed to move through life to arrange for love and it can get in the way of us fully experiencing God's love. It's familiar, it is not us, and yet it is in us. It is an operating system of hiding, proving, and fearing supported and advanced by our thoughts, habits, and routines. The false self uses strategies that seemingly protect, provide, and arrange for life, love, freedom, and belovedness.

> ### In order to discover who we are, we need to discover who we aren't.
> **- Michael Thompson, *The Heart of a Warrior***

If you don't recognize the False Self operating in you, it's probably running the show.

> ### A man can be so fooled, so tricked into believing his false self is his real self, that he isn't ever ready to fight against [contend with] it. Like an old shirt, it becomes comfortable and even indispensable.
> **- Michael Thompson, *The Heart of a Warrior***

Do you know what the only good news about the False Self is? The False Self is FALSE ... it isn't the true you, but it will lead you, drive you, or hide you ... if you let it.

Consider ...

The temptation when we find ourselves face-to-face with something unfamiliar or disconcerting or downright uncomfortable about ourselves or our circumstances is to move on as quickly as possible. What do you do with your shame, fear, anxiety, or the presence of grief or regret, disappointment or anger?

In which of these four scenarios is there hope?

False Self // False Self

False Self // True Self

True Self // False Self

True Self // True Self

There is hope in every scenario in which a True Self is present!

Where are YOU hiding?

Often, we identify ourselves by what we do - by roles we have taken on and stepped into - wife, mom, teacher, runner, boss, military wife, church volunteer, small group leader, care giver. Your role is not who you are.

What about roles you've stepped into that seem as natural as breathing? Or maybe, think about what others say about you, or said about you as a child. Are you ...

- the one who always comes through

- the one who always takes care of everything

  and everyone

- the quiet one

- the good one

- the funny one

- the perfectionist

- the successful one

- the emotional one

- the smart one

- the adventurous one

- the wounded one

- the victim

- the peacekeeper

- the disruptive one

- the one who plans for everything that could

  possibly go wrong

- the one who always understands and listens

- the one everyone just uses

- _____

The False Self allows us to avoid the deepest questions of our hearts, always keeping us at arm's length from our True Self. And when we don't know our deepest, Truest Self, we can miss God and what He has for us. God created our True Self, and God invites this True Self into deep relationship with Himself.

Movie Night ...

Watch the films *Little, My Big Fat Greek Wedding,* or *The Proposal,* and observe how Jackie, Tula, and Margaret are each hiding differently. **What do their stories stir in your heart?**

_____

_____

_____

_____

_____

_____

Conversation with Friends ...

As a group, take turns sharing your responses to the video and these questions.

1. What are some roles you have stepped into as an adult? Were there roles you felt you had to step into as a child? What were they?

2. Describe the False Self you see operating in your life. What situations provoke the False Self in you?

3. The False Self in Sherry came against the False Self in her husband, and they clashed. That clash, left unchecked for fourteen years, led to their divorce. Do you see how the False Self operating in you can provoke the False Self in someone close to you? Share a story of a recent collision.

Time Alone with God

Before the next gathering, carve out time to be still. Find a quiet place, and bring the questions of your heart to God.

1. Father, as a child, how did my young heart respond to experiencing that I needed to be different than I was made by you to be?

2. Holy Spirit, what is the False Self's way of securing love, of hiding, proving, and fearing, of moving in the world when I feel shame?

3. Jesus, what are my habits, routines, reactions, and ways that reinforce the False Self operating in me?

Stories from the Journey: Robin Responds

It is helpful for me to think of the False Self as unhealthy styles of relating to others that were born out of moments when I experienced harm, betrayal, shame, or loss. Moments when I felt *unprotected*.

In order to protect myself from further harm or pain, I unknowingly put in place defensive structures to keep myself safe and to arrange for love and connection.

I learned to hide how I was truly feeling.

I shut down and stayed quiet.

I kept my thoughts, opinions, and feelings to myself. They were safer locked away.

I made myself small and manageable, complacent, and "nice." I became a good girl.

I lightened relational tension by being funny. If I could distract someone from their anger or from their demand to be right and agreed with, then I had a better chance of staying safe and keeping the peace.

I believe it is important to consider our styles of relating - our False Self - with curiosity and kindness. After all, our young selves endured quite a lot. We were trying to survive, trying to stay alive, and desperately needing to be loved and protected.

It is important to draw the distinction between death TO self and death OF self. "... people view death to self as if it means getting rid of yourself. That is not at all what it involves. You were not put here on earth to get rid of yourself. you were put here to be a self, and to live fully as a self. The worth of the self – your self – is inestimable, and God's intent for you is that you become a fully realized self [TRUE SELF] as you make the grace fueled movement from the old self to the new (Colossians 3:9-10)."

- Dallas Willard, Life without Lack

Stories from the Journey: Dana Responds

Wide awake late into the night after watching Session 2, I heard God's invitation to me, to us, His beloved - an invitation to a holy deconstruction.

Is this our God speaking about the past, prophesying the future? Both?

His invitation:

> *"What if I allowed circumstances to come into your life that would kindly deconstruct the world you have created for yourself? (That you created to protect yourself from any further hurt or harm.) What if I kindly took your hand and brought you into the ruined places? Into the scenes that you fear most from your past or into the tyranny of your imagined future?*
>
> *And what if, when we arrived at these scenes, I helped you to take off your mask and deconstructed your perimeter, we stood just there together—naked and unashamed?*
>
> *And what if in that place, you discovered that I was enough for you there, right there? What if you discovered that you are actually tender and strong; that you are resilient and glorious?! What if you found that instead of keeping yourself, you discovered that I am keeping you?!*
>
> *What if, in this offer of deconstruction, you found treasures in this darkness; found what is TRUE and indestructible: True about you (the way I made you), true about Me (who created your glorious self and who keeps you in ALL circumstances)?*
>
> *What if you found that I am your perimeter—your wall of protection—that I am clothing you more beautifully than the lilies of the field and with the armor of God?!*
>
> *What if the walls you built have been keeping you from the MORE that I have for you? Have been keeping you from becoming fully who I created you to be in this world?*
>
> *What if you took me up on this offer of holy deconstruction, of taking you into these ruined places so that we could rebuild together?*
>
> *How would that be?*
>
> *Will you take my hand?"*

I'm so glad to be on this journey with you!

Extra Notes - Session 2

_____

_____

_____

_____

_____

_____

_____

_____

_____

_____

_____

_____

_____

_____

_____

_____

_____

_____

_____

Going Deeper ...

There is so much more to discover and consider in your journey, exploration, and increasing awareness of the false self ways and your truest self. Resources that we've found significant in our journey:

The Sacred Romance, by Brent Curtis and John Eldredge

True You: Letting Go of Your False Self to Uncover the Person God Created, by Michelle DeRusha

Immortal Diamond: The Search for Our True Self, by Richard Rohr

wounded:
the loss of eden

Holy places are dark places. It is life and strength, not knowledge and words, that we get in them. Holy wisdom is not clear and thin like water, but thick and dark like blood.

C.S. Lewis, *Till We Have Faces*

No tale of woe?

Mr. Rochester, *Jane Eyre* (2011 film)

In this session, we are invited to consider going back into our stories - into the beauty and the brokenness, the joy and the pain, the places where the False Self was created, and Eden was lost.

Review: Where did the False Self Come From?

The False Self is born from the wounds and trauma we have experienced in our lives. It's a means of self-protection, a way for us to hide, a way to attempt to keep ourselves safe. Like a mask, the False Self prevents us from being known for who we truly are.

The False Self comes from the places in our hearts that were missed and harmed. Where we were wounded, as little girls or as adults, long ago, and just yesterday.

> **The thief comes only in order to steal and kill and destroy. I have come that they may have life, and have it in abundance.**
> **- John 10:10**

> **The Spirit of the Lord is upon me, because He has anointed me to bring good news to the poor. He has sent me to proclaim release to captives, and recovery of sight to the blind, to set free those who are oppressed, to proclaim the favorable year of the Lord.** - Luke 4:18-19

Going Back Into Our Story

Let's go back into our stories, specifically the places in our hearts that have been wounded, to find out what has gotten in the way of knowing our worth and how deeply we are loved.

Consider ...

How were you named? Where is there shame in your story? How did you learn to shut your heart down? This is where we are being invited to linger for a little while.

Why remember? Why return to times that were so painful? ... The answer is simple and often not compelling to the person in pain: because our past, especially our pain, holds the key to our future and to the joy set before us. Our past is a treasure map that, read well, can lead us to vast abundance.

- Dan Allender, *The Healing Path*

The story of any one of us is in some measure the story of us all.

- Frederick Beuchner

Do you see your story in that of Jane Eyre? Or in Dana's story? In moments of wounding, harm, and loss, we are *renamed*.

When Jesus arrived in the villages of Caesarea Philippi, he asked his disciples, "What are people saying about who the Son of Man is?"

They replied, "Some think he is John the Baptizer, some say Elijah, some Jeremiah or one of the other prophets."

He pressed them, "And how about you? Who do you say I am?"

Simon Peter said, "You're the Christ, the Messiah, the Son of the living God."

Jesus came back, "God bless you, Simon, son of Jonah! You didn't get that answer out of books or from teachers. My Father in heaven, God himself, let you in on this secret of who I really am. And now I'm going to tell you who you are, really are. You are Peter, a rock. This is the rock on which I will put together my church, a church so expansive with energy that not even the gates of hell will be able to keep it out.

- Matthew 16:13-18

God wants to uncover these three things in our lives:

WHO IS GOD?

WHO ARE YOU REALLY?

HOW ARE YOU TO BE NAMED IN HIS PRESENCE?

Harm exists across a wide spectrum, from *I had a pretty good childhood, I'm not really wounded* to *If you knew how bad, how dark my story is, you would run far away from me.*

This is important for our hearts to acknowledge: *all* harm and brokenness is a violation of what we were created for, which is unfettered intimacy. We were made for delight and for honor.

Comparisons like *"What you suffered is way worse than what I have experienced,"* are not helpful. **They minimize our own stories of harm and distance us from what happened to us.**

> **The leaders and prophets of Israel who were clearly chosen and blessed all lived very broken lives. And we, the beloved sons and daughters of God, cannot escape brokenness either.**
>
> **- Henri Nouwen, *Life of the Beloved***

The words of the reckless pierce like swords ...

Solomon in Proverbs 12:18

Those I love have turned against me ...

Jeremiah 19:19a

Don't call me Naomi (Pleasant One), call me Mara (Bitter) ... I went away full, but the Lord has brought me home empty ...

Naomi in Ruth 1:20-21

Woe is me, I am undone ...

Isaiah 6:5

My God, My God, Why have you abandoned me? Why are you so far away when I groan for help?

David, Psalm 22 (and Jesus)

Let the day of my birth be erased ...

Job 3:3

My soul is deeply troubled ...

Jesus in John 12:27

My own pain in life has taught me that the first step to healing is not a step away from the pain, but a step toward it. - Henri Nouwen

We need to go back into our stories, particularly our stories of harm. There is something in your story that Jesus wants you to name, that he may show you how he wants to/will redeem it.

Like Jane Eyre, we distance ourselves from the pain of the past and our tale of woe.

Part of the definition of Shalom is "to destroy the authority that binds to chaos." When Shalom is shattered through wounds, we experience chaos in one form or another.

THE WOUNDS EFFECT

Wounding Moment	The Agreement	The Vow
The message (lie) ➡	"I'm not ..." =	"I will always ..."
Arrow to the heart	"I'm too ..."	"I will never ..."

For Example ...

Wounding Moment	The Agreement	The Vow
My father left ... ➡	"I'm on my own." =	"I will never trust anyone again."

Consider ...

Dana shared that

Evil wishes to ruin beauty, intimacy, and union.

Evil wants to ruin my capacity to receive.

Evil wants me to lose my sense of power.

How have you experienced this in your life?

Read the story of Tamar in 2 Samuel 13-14.

Tamar never got justice. She never got healing. She never went to the king who could have helped her, and the king was her own father!

Her story could have ended so differently if she had gone to the king. He had the power to give Tamar justice and a second chance at a good life. He had the power as King of Israel to redeem her.

Consider ...

What have you hidden?

What have you been afraid or ashamed to speak of or name?

What if we don't go there?

To honestly *name* the harm/brokenness in God's presence sets us on the road to healing.

The quickest way for anyone to reach the sun and the light of day is NOT to run west, chasing after the setting sun, but to head east into the darkness until one comes to the sunrise.

- Jerry Sittser, A Grace Disguised

It is the accumulated losses of a lifetime that slowly weigh us down - the times of rejection, the moments of isolation - when we felt cut off from the sustaining touch of comfort and love. It is an ache that resides in the heart, the faint echo calling us back to the times of loss. We are called back, not so much to make things right, but to acknowledge what happened to us. Grief asks that we honor the loss and, in doing so, deepen our capacity for compassion. When grief remains unexpressed, however, it hardens, becomes as solid as a stone.

We, in turn, become rigid and stop moving in rhythm with the soul. When our grief stagnates, we become fixed in place, unable to move and dance with the flow of life. Grief is part of the dance. **- Richard Rohr**

Until we go back into our stories, our wounds will remain unnamed, the messages we received from the wounds and agreements we've made will go unchallenged, and resulting vows will continue to shape how we live our lives.

Set aside time before the next gathering to take your heart and your journal to God. Time to open the trunk and rummage through all that has been locked away for so long. Time to name your wounds - to see the agreements and vows you have made, keeping you from healing and restoration. The most beautiful thing about walking in this direction is that Jesus is waiting for you there.

Movie Night ...

Watch the films *Jane Eyre* and *A Little Chaos*. **What do these stories resonate with in you?**

Conversation with Friends ...

As a group, take turns sharing your responses to the video and these questions.

1. Why is it so hard for us to go to the places in our stories that are the most painful? What are you afraid of finding there?

2. What if we don't go there? Think about Tamar and living her whole life as a desolate woman. How might her life have been different had she gone to the king (her father) for justice and redemption? Now put yourself in her shoes. Does it feel easier or safer to continue to hide? What is the risk of speaking your truth?

3. What does it look like for you to head East into the darkness, but with the promise that Jesus is waiting for you right there? What does that do to your heart? What rises in you with this "dark but lovely" invitation?

Time Alone with God

Before the next gathering, carve out time to be still. Find a quiet place, and bring the questions of your heart to God.

1. Father God, what is my tale of woe? Where did I feel vulnerable and unprotected as a young girl? Will you show me ...

Did I feel unseen? Invisible?
Was there a scene of abandonment?
Did I experience physical abuse? Emotional abuse? Sexual abuse? Rape?
What has been stolen from me?
What has been silenced in me?
What have I lost?
How do I see my younger self who experienced these things?
How do I speak to her?

2. Jesus, how have my wounds named me? Where do I feel shame in my story?

3. Holy Spirit, what are the vows and agreements I made in the wounding moments?

Stories from the Journey: Lenné Responds

We think of wounds as being the result of a harmful thing done to us; but for me in my story, it begins not with what someone did, but what they failed to do. I know, that I know, that I know, that my mom and dad love me. They demonstrated that in so many ways. And while that's true, it is also true that the deep wounding of their hearts created in them an inability (unawareness?) that perpetuated wounding across generations.

My mom was an only child. Her father was a career marine who served in World War 2. Most of his unit was killed in battle and he lived the rest of his life with survivor's guilt. He died when my mom was nine; but honestly, he was not very present to her before he died due to the guilt he felt. So mom was essentially raised by a single mom who had to figure out how to make her way in the world with a child in tow and no help from anyone. That required both my grandmother and my mom to become very strong and independent. As a child, mom learned to figure things out for herself, to not need instruction. When she became my mom, she also fostered in my sister and me a view of independence. Practically, that meant she wasn't big on life instruction about things outside of school, things like the heart. Dad neither. They provided little to no modeling about the mechanics of relationships. Neither of my parents had close friends. They were friendly enough and certainly had church acquaintances (they would've called them friends), but there was no one they depended on or confided in very deeply. Consequently, my parents gave no instruction on friendship, on marriage, on conflict resolution, on many things. The message to my young heart was "figure it out". And that was terrifying and lonely.

The lack of words extended to so many issues - things I needed help with. One of those was the issue of beauty. Nothing was ever spoken about that as a general concept or as specifically applied to me, or my sister, or my mom. We didn't grow up in a home where anyone told us how pretty we were. It wasn't that we were told awful things about ourselves, but rather that there was just dead silence on the issue. There was no validation of the concept of beauty, no view that the desire and longing for beauty was legitimate. So when the world spoke into beauty, I had no basis for response. As the world began to define what was beautiful, and I heard my enemy whisper that I didn't qualify; that I had too much of this and too little of that; I had no defense for that.

Ultimately, where that led was an ongoing wound and unanswered question over my heart about whether I had any beauty to offer. And not knowing the answer, I began to very lopsidedly focus on the one thing about me that seemed to stand out - my mind. That's what all the adults in my life pointed to as having value. It took many years to discover that my value goes far beyond that. In fact, it is only recently that God has begun to address the pain I feel over the beauty issue.

Extra Notes - Session 3

Going Deeper ...

There is so much more to discover and consider in your journey, exploration, and increasing awareness of how we've experienced wounding. Resources that we've found significant in our journey:

Life of the Beloved, by Henri Nouwen

Run with Horses, by Eugene Peterson

The Healing Path, by Dan Allender

A Grace Disguised, by Jerry Sittser

The Cure for Sorrow, Jan Richardson

healing:
a path toward eden

Let Something Essential Happen to Me

Oh, God,
let something essential happen to me,
something more than interesting
or entertaining,
or thoughtful.
O God,
let something essential happen to me,
something awesome,
something real.
Speak to my condition, Lord,
and change me somewhere inside where it matters,
a change that will burn and tremble and heal
and explode me into tears
or laughter
or love that throbs or screams
or keeps a terrible, cleansing silence
and dares the dangerous deeds.
Let something happen in me
which is my real self, God...

Ted Loder, *Guerillas of Grace*

In this session, we consider what it might look like to experience Jesus' presence, his comfort, his care, his healing - in the midst of the darkness, and in the places of our pain. Engaging with Jesus on the path towards our healing is an essential part of the restoration of our True Self ... tasting Eden!

The wounds we have endured, their impact, the messages that came with them, and the way we handled them do not have to have the final word. They *do not* have to be the end of the story!

> **The Spirit of the Sovereign LORD is on me, because the LORD has anointed me to proclaim good news to the poor. He has sent me to heal the wounds of/bind up the brokenhearted, to proclaim freedom for the captives and release from darkness for the prisoners/those who are bound, to comfort all who mourn, to care for the needs of those who grieve - to bestow on them a crown of beauty in the place of ashes, the oil of joy instead of tears, and the mantle of joyous praise instead of the spirit of heaviness/despair. Because of this, they will be known as/renamed Mighty Oaks of Righteousness, planted by Yahweh as a living display of his glory/splendor.**
>
> **- from Isaiah 61 (compilation of translations)**

Jesus came to heal the brokenhearted. He wants healing for us. He came to restore the *Shalom* (wholeheartedness) we were made for.

Consider ...

Strong's Concordance translates the original Hebrew of "heal the brokenhearted" as ...

to heal/bind up means to: wrap, bandage, give relief, to heal - namely a wound

the broken - crushed, smashed, torn down, demolished, destroyed, shattered, fractured, hurt, injured, broken into pieces

heart[ed] - the inner part of a person - soul, heart, mind, memory, thoughts, conscience, will, understanding, the seat of emotions and passions and seat of courage

---

Jesus came, and continues to come, to bring his kind healing and tend to our wounded and broken hearts, minds, and beings, *and* He invites us to join Him in the healing process.

Healing is when our truest self is being restored, welcomed, uncovered, unbound, let up for air, cared for, nourished, and set free.

> ***Gather my broken fragments to a whole ... Let mine be a merry, all-receiving heart, but make it a whole, with light in every part.***
>
> **- George Macdonald**

Consider ...

What should we do with our pain? Should we ignore it? Should we just "get over it"? Should we optimistically hope that everything will work out in the end? What have you done with your pain?

> ***If we fail to respond appropriately to the wounds that life and relationships inflict, our pain will be wasted; it will numb us or destroy us. But suffering doesn't have to mangle our hearts and rob us of joy. It can, instead, lead us to life - if we know the path to healing.***
>
> ***Healing is not the resolution of our past; it is the use of our past to draw us into deeper relationship with God and his purposes for our lives.***
>
> **- Dan Allender, *The Healing Path***

Awareness does not equal healing. Pay attention. Be aware of what you are experiencing when tears come, when anger comes, when you're tender, or where you're hurting or feel stuck.

Being aware that something happened to us in our story that hurt us, affected us, and continues to affect us is the first step towards healing.

Jesus wants to bring true healing, not just relief. He wants to show us a better way, a kinder way, a truer way. He wants to join us in the hurt, the pain, and the discomfort of it and show us how to move in this with Him.

Consider ...

What if Jesus wants to explore with you how you have handled your own young self in the process?

Our bodies remember what we experienced, so naming what happened, what we experienced, and the particularities (such as what my body felt) is very significant.

When we dismiss or diminish parts of our story, we actually are preventing our healing. Will you allow yourself to be curious about your story, your memories, your wounding moments?

> **There is no way to experience healing apart from taking an honest look at those stories that hold intense feelings such as shame, powerlessness, terror, a sense of betrayal.** - Adam Young

God can bring healing in an instant IF and WHEN he so chooses, yet more often, he invites us to explore with him a little deeper, as often there are other things connected and styles of relating (like the False Self) that need untangling.

The harm we endured was against our body/soul/spirit. *Healing and Integration also happens within that body/soul/spirit. So we must engage our body and our soul (heart, mind, will, imagination) in the healing process. It's how God designed it to work.*

Our bodies were brilliantly designed by God. We hold in every cell, in every bit of our DNA, everything that has happened to us. Our bodies hold both the good and the bad, when we have known delight and honor, and when we have known harm and abuse.

Our bodies were never meant to experience harm. *Remember:* we were meant to experience safety, goodness, delight, and honor.

Our bodies hold the pain and trauma deep inside, and cue us when attention and care are needed. We can't escape it! We can deny it, we can try to bury it, and numb it, but our brilliant bodies will let us know what needs tending to, what needs healing.

What if some of the physical conditions we experience are results of unhealed emotional, psychological, and physical trauma?

We have been formed by our relationships and by levels of danger and/or security within those relationships. And wonderfully, healing often happens in the context of safe, loving relationships.

Consider ...

A trigger is a stimulus that elicits a reaction, setting off a memory or flashback. Triggers are very personal; different things trigger different people. One often will react to this trigger with an emotional intensity similar to that of the time of the trauma. A person's triggers are activated through one or more of the five senses: sight, sound, touch, smell and taste.

How do you feel in your body when you experience this?

Consider ...

When and where have you known shame and contempt for yourself?

What if we could choose to interrupt the shame and contempt cycle and move a little closer to our younger self? What if we approach her with curiosity and with kindness, instead of shame and contempt?

71

We will not be able to experience healing in those memories if we are standing in judgment, with contempt, and blaming our young self. Only as we regard her with curiosity, kindness, tenderness, and care will there be an opportunity for healing.

> ***Kindness begins the healing process as it soothes ambivalence, engages our heart, and calls our soul to wholeness.***
>
> **- Dan Allender, *Healing the Wounded Heart***

When we are able to consider our stories with sorrow and grief on behalf of our young self and what she endured, and when we allow tears to come for her and the sorrow that she didn't get what she needed in those moments, *this opens the door to healing, integration, and restoration.*

Anger can be an important part of grief. What if we allow ourselves to experience appropriate anger for what happened to us, for what we didn't get that we desperately needed, for what we suffered? *Grief and anger are necessary for transformation and healing.*

We cannot offer our children what we have not experienced ourselves. We can't take someone further than we've been willing to go ourselves.

Consider ...

What has your experience been? What did your young self need and not get? Can you locate your young self in your story? What keeps you from seeing her?

You do not make it to adulthood in this broken, fractured, sin-laden world without experiencing hurt, heartache, and harm. Your young self needs the advocate that she didn't have in those wounding moments.

Grief is the body's natural response to seeing the truth of the heartbreak of your story. To enter into the grief is to allow the full range of emotions, including anger.

Receiving good care brings healing.

It can be incredibly healing when we hear. "I believe you. It's not your fault." *The wounds that happened to you are not your fault.*

Tears can be so healing. They help to open and cleanse the wound.

The tears ... streamed down, and I let them flow as freely as they would, making of them a pillow for my heart. On them it rested.

- St. Augustine, *Confessions*

There are layers to healing. Oftentimes we are brought back to a story where something else needs to be explored, named, grieved, and tended to. And a deeper level of healing can be experienced. God brings healing to our injured hearts in countless ways. Healing is not linear.

> ***No one's healing path is the same, yet the terrain is similar. Faith grows to the degree that we do what seems counterintuitive: open our heart to remember, grieve, and ask God to engage our anguish with tenderness. This is a healing path that is life-giving, freeing, and empowering.***
>
> **- Dan Allender, *Healing the Wounded Heart***

Healing may come through sharing in the presence of comfort and care. Kindness involves learning to trust our body and our stories in the presence of another person.

Consider ...

Find a counselor or a friend who is able to sit with you as you share your story. Healing often comes when they ...

Honor your story by listening intently - holding that space for you and bearing witness to the harm you experienced.

Ask questions that lead to deeper exploration without trying to give advice or fix you or pop you up out of the discomfort or drag you to joy.

Allow silence sometimes.

Have tears on behalf of your young self who was so wounded ... that perhaps invites your own tears and grief.

All of this opens the door for healing. In the presence of kindness and care, healing is possible.

These can be holy moments.

If you are unsure how to find a good counselor, start by reviewing Zoweh's list of recommended counselors at zoweh.org/counseling-services.

Jesus invites us to experience his presence, his comfort, his care, his healing - in the midst of the darkness, and in the places of our pain. To shepherd our hearts to bring integration and wholeheartedness, to become healed, whole, our *full* humanity restored!

The Holy Spirit is always bringing healing. And in these spaces, we always *need* and always *have* the Presence, the wisdom, the discernment and the help of the Holy Spirit, who is our most wonderful counselor and mothering presence. We need and we have the supernatural power and kindness of God that brings deep healing, restoration, transformation, and life to the full in greater measure.

> *Praise be to the God and Father of our Lord Jesus Christ, the Father of compassion and the God of all comfort, who comforts us in all our troubles, so that we can comfort those in any trouble with the comfort we ourselves receive from God.*
>
> **- 2 Corinthians 1:3-4**

Jesus knows what we have endured. He knows what we bear in our bodies and our souls. Jesus is referred to as a Man of Sorrows. He sympathizes with us, weeps with us when we weep, and comforts us.

> *Blessed are they who mourn, for they will be comforted.*
>
> **- Matthew 5:4**

Conversation with Friends ...

As a group, take turns sharing your responses to the video and these questions.

1. Share what rises up in you when you hear, *"The wounds we have endured, their impact, the messages that came with them, and the way we handled them do not have to have the final word. They do not have to be the end of the story!"*

2. Can you think of something in your story (a memory) that you have dismissed or diminished that you are realizing now might actually be important to consider and invite Jesus to bring healing to? Would you like to share about it?

3. What is one thing that your young self needed but did not get? (care? protection? advocacy?)

Time Alone with God

Before the next gathering, carve out time to be still. Find a quiet place, and bring the questions of your heart to God.

Lord Jesus, I invite you into this time with me. Please meet me here in this space.

What is one wounding moment/tale of woe/story of heartbreak where you want to experience healing?

Will you allow yourself to close your eyes and remember the story ... will you allow yourself to enter the memory ... and to remember the particularities of the environment. What were you feeling in that moment? Take some time here.

What might make it difficult for you to stay in the emotions that Jesus brings up?

Will you allow yourself to name - put words to - what you felt/feel? Is it pain? Sadness? Fear? Disgust? Sorrow? Anger? Rage? Shame? Despair?

Are you able to sit with those emotions for one or two minutes?

Can you let yourself grieve what was lost? What was stolen?

_____
_____
_____

What do you feel toward your young self in that space?

_____
_____
_____

Allow yourself to fully feel how you feel toward her. Writing it out may help to put words to it.

_____
_____
_____
_____

What did she need in that moment? Can you name what she needed?

_____
_____
_____
_____

Grief is met by the comfort of God. If this is true, where do you need comfort? Are you able to risk asking God for comfort? What would you want that to look like? Feel like?

_____
_____
_____
_____

What are you longing for in this moment?

_____
_____
_____
_____

Jesus, would you please bring healing to the places that are tender, hurting, that feel vulnerable. (If you are able ...) I give you permission to come and tend to my mind/body/heart/soul. Bring care to my young self and my self at every age where I experienced wounding and harm. Bind up the broken places. Bring the shattered pieces to wholeness. Restore my life. Restore my hope. Show me your Great Love in this place.

Stories from the Journey: Lenné Responds

The amount of healing we can receive from God is limited by how much pain we're willing to acknowledge and allow into our awareness. If we don't let ourselves know our pain and bring it to God, we don't give God permission and space to heal it.

I love these lines from the song "Your Will, Your Way," by Brian and Katie Torwalt ...

> *You are the river that won't run dry,*
> *There is no desert Your streams won't find;*
> *Wherever it runs, hearts come alive,*
> *River flow through me, river flow through me ...*

Going Deeper ...

There is so much more to discover and consider in your healing journey. Resources that we've found significant in our journey:

Become Good Soil podcast #070: The Body Keeps the Score, with Morgan & Cherie Snyder

The Body Keeps the Score, by Bessel Van Der Kolk

The Allender Center podcast, episode "Practicing Kindness: Trauma and the Body"

The Place We Find Ourselves podcast with Adam Young, episodes "How Healing Happens, Parts 1-3," "The U-Diagram with Cathy Loerzel," and "Your Wounds and the Path to Healing"

the story we find ourselves in

Toto, I've got a feeling we're not in Kansas anymore.

Dorothy Gale, *The Wizard of Oz* (1939 film)

If you don't understand the Larger Story that your personal story is in, you'll not only miss the Larger Story, but you won't - you can't - live well in your own story.

Michael Thompson, *Search and Rescue*

In this session, we begin to look at the Larger Story our stories are set in, and the significance of orientation: knowing who we are, where we are, and the good God is up to in our lives.

Restoration

Humanity and Creation are being restored, and one day, will all be made new.

Orientation

Ginóskó: to know through personal experience.

We have a deeper, truer knowing when we encounter God and experience him.

Being an *oriented* woman means knowing and experiencing with God these three things ...

Who You Are;
Where You Are; and
The Good That God Is Up To in Your Life.

Being *disoriented* is that feeling of not knowing what's going on around you or how you got where you are. Sometimes it's subtle, like a gnawing in your mind; other times, it's jarring, as if the whole world got flipped upside-down, like in trauma.

We all experience disorientation at points in our lives. In the spiritual realm, there is a battle raging - all for the alliance, allegiance, and affection of your heart. It started with Adam and Eve in Genesis 3, and still carries on for all of us now.

Where Are We?

In every story, there's a context to the story and there's a relationship between the characters and the environments they're in.

> *Look carefully then how you walk! Live purposefully and worthily and accurately, not as the unwise and witless, but as wise (sensible, intelligent people), making the very most of the time [buying up each opportunity], because the days are evil.*
> **- Ephesians 5:15-16**

2 REALMS

2 KINGDOMS

If we discover a desire within us that nothing in this world can satisfy, we should begin to wonder if perhaps we were created for another world.

C.S. Lewis

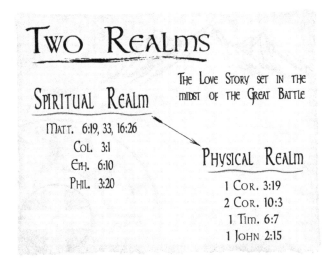

TWO REALMS

SPIRITUAL REALM

THE LOVE STORY SET IN THE MIDST OF THE GREAT BATTLE

MATT. 6:19, 33, 16:26
COL. 3:1
EPH. 6:10
PHIL. 3:20

PHYSICAL REALM

1 COR. 3:19
2 COR. 10:3
1 TIM. 6:7
1 JOHN 2:15

Spiritual Realm

Eyes to See and Ears to Hear

Matthew 6:19 - Where your treasure is, there your heart will be also.
Matthew 6:33 - Seek first the Kingdom of God.
Matthew 16:26 - What good will it be for a man if he gains the whole world yet forfeits his soul?
Colossians 3:1 - Since then, you have been raised with Christ, set your hearts on things above.
Ephesians 6:12 - Our struggle is not against flesh and blood, but against rulers, against the authorities, against the powers of this dark world and against the spiritual forces of evil in the heavenly realms.
Philippians 3:20 - But our citizenship is in heaven. And we eagerly await a Savior from there, the Lord Jesus Christ.

Physical Realm

The scriptures talk about marriage, relationships, conflict, finances, parenting, work, intimacy, They also encourage us with a vantage point of the Spiritual Realm.

1 Corinthians 3:19 - For the wisdom of this world is foolishness in God's sight.
2 Corinthians 10:3 - For though we live in the world we do not wage war as the world does.
1 Timothy 6:7 - For we brought nothing into the world, and we can take nothing out of it.
1 John 2:15 - Do not love the world or anything in the world.

KINGDOM OF DARKNESS

THE UNHOLY TRINITY → SATAN FLESH WORLD

HOW: LURING AND TEMPTING

LIES ABOUT: YOU GOD OTHERS

CENTRAL
ROMANS 10:9-10
PROVERBS 4:23
JOHN 10:10

LEADS TO: DEATH, SLAVERY, BONDAGE, FALSE SELF, POSING, FEAR, CONTROL, SHAME, GUILT, CAPTIVITY AND DEPRESSION

John 10:10 - The thief comes to steal, kill, and destroy.
1 Peter 5:8 - Be self controlled and alert. Your enemy, the devil, prowls around like a roaring lion looking for someone to devour.
John 14:30 - The prince of this dark world is coming.
2 Corinthians 11:14 - Satan masquerades as an angel of light.
John 8:44 - He is a liar and the father of lies.
WHAT IS THE POWER OF A LIE?
Revelation 12:9 - Satan leads the whole world astray *(deception)*

KINGDOM OF LIGHT

THE HOLY TRINITY

FATHER
SON △ HOLY SPIRIT

CENTRAL
ROMANS 10:9-10
PROVERBS 4:23
JOHN 10:10

TRUTH ABOUT: YOU HIMSELF OTHERS

HOW: WOOING AND PURSUING

LEADS TO: LIFE, FREEDOM, VICTORY, PURPOSE, GLORY, NEWNESS, RESTORATION, INTIMACY, AND A ROLE TO PLAY

"WALK WITH ME" --- GOD

Luke 4 - Heal the broken hearted, sight for the blind, freedom for the prisoners.
Luke 19:10 - The Son of Man came to seek and save that which was lost.
John 10:10 - He came that we might have LIFE.
Matthew 20:28 - He gave His life as a ransom.
Galatians 1:4 & 1 Corinthians 1:13 - He came to offer rescue.

THE UNHOLY TRINITY
SATAN
WORLD
FLESH

THE LARGE

LIFE, FREEDOM,

THE HEART

PHYSICAL REALM
MONEY, MARRIAGE, RELATIONSHIPS,
CONFLICTS, PARENTING, WORK

CENTRA
ROMANS 1
PROVERBS
JOHN 10

KINGDOM OF DARKNESS

WHICH KINGDOM AD

BATTLE, VIOLENCE, REV. 19,
CITIZENSHIP P

HOW:
LURING
AND
TEMPTING

WHAT YOU BEL
IT HAS AUTHORITY

LIES ABOUT:
YOU
GOD
OTHERS

LEADS TO: FALSE SELF, GUILT,   L
SHAME, FEAR, CONTROL

...ER STORY

..., RESTORATION

... IS CENTRAL

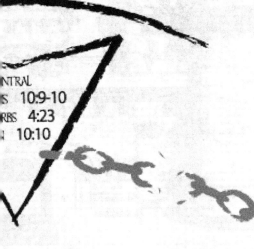

...NTRAL
...S 10:9-10
...RBS 4:23
...H 10:10

...ADVANCES AND HOW?

...V. 19, MATT. 12:25, JOSH 1:9
...P PHIL 3:20

...ELIEVE MATTERS
...ITY IN YOUR LIFE

... LEADS TO : RESTORATION, LIFE, FREEDOM
PURPOSE, INTIMACY, A ROLE TO PLAY

THE HOLY TRINITY
FATHER
SON
HOLY
SPIRIT

SPIRITUAL REALM
THE LOVE STORY SET IN THE MIDST OF A GREAT BATTLE

KINGDOM OF LIGHT

HOW:
WOOING
AND
PURSUING

TRUTH ABOUT:
YOU
GOD
OTHERS

OUR HEARTS

It is by the heart that God is perceived (known) and not by reason... so that is what faith is, God perceived by the heart

Oswald Chambers

Above all else, guard your heart, for it is the wellspring of life.

Proverbs 4:23 (NIV)

Keep vigilant watch over your heart; that's where life starts.

Proverbs 4:23 (MSG)

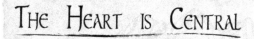

THE HEART IS CENTRAL

OUR HEARTS MATTER TO GOD!

PROVERBS 4:23
PS. 51:10
EZ. 18:31, 36:26-27
EPH. 3:17
PS. 147:3
MT. 5:8, 13:15
LUKE 6:45
HEB. 4:12

UNGER'S BIBLE DICTIONARY
THE SEAT OF EMOTIONS,
DESIRES, INTELLECT,
REASON, MOTIVES
THE DEEP WATER

DESIRES AND NEEDS OF HEART...
VALIDATION, ACCEPTANCE, WORTH, BELONGING, SIGNIFICANCE, AFFIRMATION
LOVE AND LIFE

Romans 10:9,10 - If you confess with your mouth, "Jesus is Lord," and believe in your **heart** the God raised Him from the dead, you will be saved.

1 Kings 3:9,12 - I will do what you have asked, I will give you a **wise and discerning heart**.

Jeremiah 29:13 - You will seek me and find me when you seek me with all of your **heart**.

Ezekiel 11:19 - I will give them and **undivided heart** and put a new spirit in them; I will remove from them their heart of stone and give them a **heart of flesh.**

Ezekiel 18:31 - Rid yourselves of all the offenses you have committed, and get a **new heart.**

Ezekiel 36:26,27 - I will give you a **new heart** and put a new spirit.

Ephesians 3:17 - So that Christ may dwell in your **hearts** through faith.

2 Timothy 2:22 - Flee the evil desires of youth, and pursue righteousness, faith, love and peace, along with those who call on the Lord out of **pure heart.**

Psalm 147:3 - He heals the **brokenhearted** and binds up their wounds.

Matthew 5:8 - Blessed are the **pure in heart** for they will see God.

Matthew 13:19 - When anyone hears the message about the Kingdom and does not understand it, the evil one comes and snatches away what was sown in his **heart.**

Luke 6:45 - The good man brings good things out of the good stored up in his **heart**.

Hebrews 4:12 - For the word of God is living and active ... it judges the thoughts and attitudes of the **heart.**

Psalm 51:10 - Create in me a **pure heart,** O God; and renew a steadfast spirit within me.

2 REALMS 2 KINGDOMS

Be very careful, then, how you live—not as unwise but as wise, 16 making the most of every opportunity, because the days are evil.
Ephesians 5:15-16 (NIV)

THE HeArt OF A WARRIOR

zoweh.org

The story of our lives is a *Great Adventure.* And like all great adventures, those of us who venture out get lost from time to time. It's not a matter of *if,* but *when.*

When we're lost, we slow things down, take pause and collect our thoughts. We gather our belongings and our comrades and recalibrate ourselves in attempt to answer the question, "*OK ... where are we?*"

In those times of collecting our wits and getting our bearings, a map is always an invaluable tool ... if you have one. Well, now you do. What you are holding is a *Map of the Larger Story.* A picture of the landscape in which the story of your life is contained ... The Larger Story your story is in.

At any and every given moment, your life is somewhere on the gridlines of this Larger Story. What you need in addition to this map, is the same thing all the great adventurers who have gone before you have needed: *a Guide.*
The good news is, you have one.

Open the map, take it in, take a deep breath then ask that all important question. Ask it to the one who knows where you are and wants to guide you on your next move. Ask the question, "*Where am I?*" ... and then listen.

Blessings, protection, and strength to you as you journey. I believe your next steps are about to be some of your greatest!

For LIFE in the Larger Story,

Michael Thompson
Director of Zoweh
zoweh.org

ZOWEH

And What Are We Up Against?

The enemy strategically and uniquely comes against you, your heart, and your glory. The enemy may not have arranged for all your wounding, but they can opportunistically capitalize on the wounded place to drive home deeper wounds.

Two Realms

We live right in the intersection of two realms - the spiritual and physical realms.

> **Since, then, you have been raised with Christ, set your hearts on things above, where Christ is seated at the right hand of God.**
>
> **- Colossians 3:1**

> **Our story might be best understood as the greatest love story set in the midst of the fiercest battle.**
>
> **- John Eldredge**

The Two Kingdoms, light and darkness, are at war. Jesus didn't just come to die on the cross, even though that is enormously important. He came to orient his friends.

> ## *All authority on heaven and earth has been given to me.*
> ### - Matthew 28:18

Knowing your identity in the Kingdom and *who you are* matters.

The ingredients of love ...

> **Acceptance**
>
> **Worth**
>
> **Belonging**
>
> **Significance**
>
> **Validation**

That is what love looks like, feels like, smells like.

Every little boy and every little girl is asking the same question: Do you love me and do you love what you see? This question is in our Trinity DNA. And when we take that question to wounded people and to a wounded place, what are they going to hear? No. Men take it to women. Women take it to men, and it is a train wreck. We are made for a bigger Love.

What did Solomon ask for?

> ## *Give me an understanding heart so that I can govern your people well and know the difference between right and wrong.*
> ### - 1 Kings 3:9

Your heart is central. Look at the map on pages 69-72. This is the larger story our lives are set in, and the battle is over our hearts. Your heart. The story of your life is the long and brutal assault on your heart by an enemy who knows what you could be ... and fears it.

Above all else, guard your heart, for everything you do flows from it.

- Proverbs 4:23

What you believe matters. It has authority in your life. What is the power of a lie? *That you believe it.* If you are believing a lie, and therefore living out of or building your life around that false belief, it affects the things you believe about God, about yourself, and about others.

What is the Larger Story?

The fundamental elements of the Gospel on a personal level - your sin, Jesus' death on the cross, and the forgiveness you can now receive are important to know. But if you stop there, you settle for a certain kind of life. The 'smaller story' is one in which a woman believes that the gospel is contained by a "do more, give more, sin less," focus.

We must recover [be aware of] the Larger Story if we are going to understand our own story, and step into the role God has created for us.

After all, if you don't know the Larger Story that your story is set within and how it works, then how can you play your part and live well?

Conversation with Friends ...

As a group, take turns sharing your responses to the video and these questions.

1. How do you feel about the idea that you are living in a larger story, that the context of your story is in the greatest love story set in the midst of the fiercest battle?

2. Looking at the map- what draws your eye? Why? Which concepts are new to you? Which might you want to explore more?

3. Where have you seen "what you believe matters" in your life? When have you experienced what you believe leading you to shame, fear, or control? When have you experienced what you believe leading you to healing, training, intimacy, restoration, life, freedom?

Time Alone with God

Before the next gathering, carve out time to be still. Find a quiet place, and bring the questions of your heart to God.

1. Father, what do you want me to see and experience through exploring The Larger Story Map?

2. Jesus, would you show me ways the enemy has uniquely come against me experiencing love - belonging, worth, acceptance, significance, validation?

3. Holy Spirit, where in my story have I experienced disorientation? Where, when, and how have I been lied to - about you and about myself?

Stories from the Journey: Lenné Responds

At Zoweh, we often talk about the need to know who you are, where you are, and the good that God is up to in your life. That can sound like three very separate things, but they aren't. There is a vital connection between who you are and "where." The truth is that *who* you are explains some of the *where*. When we speak of living in a Larger Story where there is a clashing of two kingdoms, and where you have a role to play, you have to understand that Father placed you very consciously and purposefully into this particular place in His story. The things that He wrote into your being, what makes you uniquely you, also makes you uniquely qualified to play the role that has your name on it. God's story needed you here, now.

Unfortunately, the enemy camp has some awareness of that. In a very real way, who you are attracts warfare because your life is dangerous for the kingdom of darkness. You are a life-bringer, a light-bearer, one who reflects the image of God and who ushers in the Kingdom of God. For the gates of hell, that's intolerable. And so the assaults come. It isn't that we need to live in fear of them. But rather armed, well prepared, and in the company of trusted companions who will lend their swords and fierce hearts.

The story of my life has contained some unexpected assaults - from places where I thought I would be safe, like church environments. Much of that assault has been due to my gender; some has been due to my gifting. I wasn't very prepared for those because I come from a family where gender never determined possibility. Neither of my parents ever communicated to me that there were things I could not do because I am female. So when various church environments began to disqualify me saying things like, "You can't teach because you're a woman," or, "You can only teach on subjects that men have already addressed," it was terribly disheartening and full of a sense of injustice. And it created the lie that there was no place for me in the Body unless I was content to sit quietly by and let men define me.

What I've come to understand about that particular assault is best described in Genesis 3:15 (The Message): "I'm declaring war between you and the Woman, between your offspring and hers. He'll wound your head, you'll wound his heel." What God says in this verse explains the unique hatred that has been leveled against women since the fall of Eden. The hatred shows up in every quarter, including politics, business, cultural rights and responsibilities, and yes, even in the Church. There is war between the kingdom of darkness and the offspring of Eve. In part, this is because the Redeemer would be born of a woman, the Redeemer who would crush the serpent's head in a final death blow. But also, the war between the daughters of Eve and the serpent is God's gift to us. That might sound odd, this thought that having battle brought to our lives is a gift. But here is the loveliness of it: We get to oppose the one who deceived us and brought us to ruin. We get to redeem Eve's terrible choice to believe the lie that Father is not good and cannot be trusted. The Trinity trusted us with a sword and is counting on us to use it well.

Extra Notes - Session 5

Going Deeper ...

There is so much more to discover and consider in your journey, exploration, and increasing awareness of the larger story. Resources that we've found significant in our journey:

Exploring More with Michael Thompson Podcast - zoweh.org/podcast

Waking the Dead, by John Eldredge

Get Your Life Back, by John Eldredge

Epic, by John Eldredge

sisterhood:
the deepening
community

When we honestly ask ourselves which people in our lives mean the most to us, we often find that it is those who, instead of giving advice, solutions, or cures, have chosen rather to share our pain and touch our wounds with a warm and tender hand.

Henri Nouwen

*Friendship is born at that moment when one person says to another:
"What! You too? I thought I was the only one!"*

C.S. Lewis

In this session, we consider the significance of living in redemptive friendships of hearts; of knowing and being known. We were created for relationships, to have friends witness and accompany us through the adventure of life.

You were not created to do this alone. We were created for relationship, for community, for knowing and being known, for intimacy with God and each other.

We were meant to taste something of the goodness of God in community with others, in a way that is nourishing, comforting, and healing. It's the way of the Kingdom.

Ministry and friendship are *not the goal*. Ministry and friendships - *sisterhood* - is the *fruit* of our intimacy with God.

Going Deeper ...

Watch the film *Captain Marvel*.

Captain Marvel's real name is Carol Danvers. She grew up on earth with a friend - and with the guidance of a good mentor, she became an Air Force pilot. After crashing an experimental aircraft and losing her memories, she believed the false stories she was told by an alien civilization and lived into that life - far from who she was and who she was created to be.

Sound familiar? They're telling our stories!

Carol has been believing the stories she's been told about herself, and the stories she's been telling herself, living a life from those lies ... until she learns the truth of who she is, from an oriented sister who reminds her who she TRULY is, and *that changes everything.*

As you move in your true identity, into who you were created to be, there will be opposition and struggle - familiar voices you've heard your whole life, particularly as you move with Jesus in friendship and sisterhood. Do you see that in your life?

As you begin to break vows and agreements and move in your True Self, in your glory, there will be an increasing settledness to your way, in your wholeheartedness. Orientation, remember? With orientation comes increasing confidence and settledness in knowing who you are, where you are, and the good God is up to in your life.

I've been fighting with one arm tied behind my back - what happens when I'm finally set free?

— Captain Marvel

What happens when YOU are becoming more free? Your strength, beauty, wholehearted intimacy with God is NEEDED in this pursuit of the hearts of other women.

Delightfully loved ones, if he loved us with such tremendous love, then "loving one another" should be our way of life!

— 1 John 4:11

The invitation is to live this way: We need friends and sisters to make it through— we need Redemptive Friendships of hearts committed to caring for one another, loving one another, listening to one another, inviting each other to be curious, and inspiring one another to the full and abundant life ... Zoweh!

The Arc - The arc over the heart symbolizes the provision and protection of God, which never fails to cover us.

The Heart - The diamond cut heart represents our hearts, which are precious, beautiful, and to be cherished, like diamonds.

Orientation: knowing and experiencing God's love in a way that restores and sets free who we truly are. The Life of the Kingdom—the Way of Freedom—is deeply opposed by the kingdom of darkness. To enjoy this restoration, we are going to have to be persistent. Many of us have experienced what it's like to be wounded in a community; and yet, it is often in community where Jesus will rescue and restore.

Redemptive Sisterhood: The journey of friendship is hard fought. **It doesn't just happen, and it doesn't just happen overnight.**

97

Redemptive Sisterhood: A Deepening Community

A small fellowship of hearts where you can know another's story, her journey and glory—to know and be known—is how we have found women best experience the love, life, and freedom for which we were created.

Here are a few of the ingredients that we've found to be important for a Redemptive Sisterhood to flourish:

Tenets of Redemptive Sisterhood ...

- Is rooted in personal **intimacy** with God
- Believes that the **redeemed heart** is good.
- Offers a safe and trusting place where **deep places** of the heart and soul can be touched.
- Pursues a woman's **glory and heart**, not her sin.
- Can't be a substitute for **God** and what only He can provide.
- Understands that the context of our story is the greatest love story set in the midst of the fiercest battle, with an enemy determined to steal, kill, and destroy.
- Must be **small and intimate.**
- Is a lifestyle where lives intersect and people share their lives together -- pray, play, worship, eat, share, and journey together. They are often intergenerational.
- Cannot be **contained** in a day, a time, or a room.
- Is a space where every woman is free to **contribute, offer,** and **participate.** No one's glory is muted.
- Will be **messy.** Don't avoid it. Enter in. Change and disruption are necessary.
- Must be **missional.** It is larger than itself.

These tenets are adaptable for redemptive marriage, redemptive parenting, and for all relationships.

Friendship, SISTERHOOD, intimacy grows through telling our stories and honoring each other's stories while holding each other's hearts through life - betrayal, death, deep grief, and longing for MORE.

Intimacy flourishes in our journey together as we experience life -- hearts, laughing together, with dear friends who love, know, and see each other, on our best days and our worst days. There is little space for the False Self- we see it coming because we know each other's True Self.

Consider ...

Sherry's friends: "Dana partnered with Jesus to awaken my heart to poetry. Robin invites me to deep places in my heart. Connie reminds me who I am ... and who I'm not. Rebecca invites me to wonder. Tracey and Ginny awaken my heart to art and call out the artist in me. I could go on and on and on about my friends and how they awaken my heart."

How have your friends awakened your heart?

How opposed is friendship? It is vitally important to have friends who truly know you.

Think about how Jesus has come for you over these six weeks. He also yearns for flourishing for the hearts of your friends, your sisters, your daughters. Will you make space and a place for the women in your lives?

Friendship - SISTERHOOD- is deeply opposed - will you fight for it?

You no longer have one arm tied behind your back, friends, you are free. Will you walk in freedom and flourishing?

Conversation with Friends ...

As a group, take turns sharing your responses to the video and these questions.

1. Have you experienced friendship/sisterhood this way? Share about it.

2. How have you experienced opposition to friendship? Schedules, loss, betrayal, etc.

3. Read the Redemptive Sisterhood Tenets. Which one(s) intrigue you? Which have you experienced?

Time Alone with God

Before the next gathering, carve out time to be still. Find a quiet place, and bring the questions of your heart to God.

1. Father, where have I been wounded in friendship?

2. Jesus, You yearn for flourishing in my life and relationships. What is in the way of my deep friendships? Where have I not allowed my true self to be seen and known?

3. Holy Spirit, in my deepest heart, I yearn for deep friendship. Who might I invite into exploring more together?

Extra Notes - Session 6

continuing your deepening journey

Intimacy is knowing and being known. What does it look like for you to continue your Deepening Journey and experience Redemptive Sisterhood together? There are LOTS of ways to continue to get to know each other. Here are some ways we've enjoyed deepening our friendships:

Tell Your Stories

As a group, what if you took the time to share your stories? Taking the time, allowing each woman an entire session to share her story, inviting the remaining women to practice the extravagant listening we're learning is invaluable in cultivating intimacy - in being seen and known. **We've included a story timeline starting on page 105 to guide you back into your story.**

Movie Nights

Movies are like modern day parables, many illustrating the epic stories of our lives. What if you, individually or as a group, intentionally watched movies? We've provided a list of some of the movies that our hearts and stories resonated with, bringing the themes of our lives to life on the big screen, awakening something epic in us.

Doing Life Together

Spend time together doing the things you love. Cooking classes, art museums, walks in the park, coffee, yoga, the list of possibilities is endless.

Make it a Family Thing

Consider inviting your husbands in by having dinner together as couples or gather your families through a picnic together. Attend each other's children's ball games, concerts, and recitals.

Explore More with Zoweh

Read and talk through Zoweh's Four Pillars on **zoweh.org/the-four-pillars-of-zoweh**

1: Intimacy, Oneness, Connectedness with God
2: Orientation - Who You are, Where You Are, and the Good God is Up to in Your Life
3: Nothing to Hide, Nothing to Prove, Nothing to Fear
4: More Love, More Life, More Freedom

The Deepening Weekend

Roadtrip! Make it a girls weekend by finding an upcoming *Deepening Weekend* to experience the significance of getting away together in a beautiful place with Jesus. See upcoming dates on **zoweh.org/events.**

The Deepening Experience

You're invited into MORE - more love, more life, more freedom. We believe this cannot be contained in a single event, resource, group, or experience, but rather as a lifetime journey of pressing in that creates intimacy with God and community with others. Visit **TheDeepeningExperience.com** to learn more.

The Deepening Community

Join the conversation with hearts around the world through The Deepening Community. Visit **TheDeepeningExperience.com** and join The Deepening Community Facebook group.

The Bible App

With over 500 million downloads, the Bible App is an easy way to invite women into exploring this message together. Invite women to journey with you through one of *The Deepening Experience* reading plans at **Bible.com.**

Counseling

Living in this fallen place can be challenging, and we all need help from those who specialize in walking with hearts through trauma and difficult histories. Consider exploring your story with a counselor who will help you connect with the heart of God and see you through the difficult parts of your journey. Counselors who have aided us in our journey can be found on **zoweh.org/counseling-services.**

THE STORY TIMELINE

CHILDHOOD (ages 0-12)

In the space below, write down some thoughts, moments, experiences, emotions, people, and events from the time you were born till the time you were about twelve years old. Here are some questions to help guide you on your way:

Who were some significant people in your life during that time? Were they helpful, or hurtful?

What events during this time, no matter how minor or major, had an effect on your life?

What did you learn from the people and circumstances in your life during this time?

What were some of your favorite things to do, see, or be during this time?

What was your school situation like? Did you enjoy it?

What was your relationship like with your parents, siblings, and/or guardians?

The Story Timeline is adapted from our friends at The Noble Heart Ministries in Colorado Springs, CO.

THE STORY TIMELINE

MIDDLE CHILDHOOD TO YOUNG ADULTHOOD (ages 12-20)

Write down some thoughts, moments, experiences, emotions, people, and events from the time you were twelve till the time you were about twenty years old. It's okay if there is some overlap from the Childhood section. Here are some questions to help guide you on your way:

Who were some significant people in your life during that time? Were they helpful, or hurtful?

What events during this time, no matter how minor or major, had an effect on your life?

What did you learn from the people and circumstances in your life during this time?

What were some of your favorite things to do, see, or be during this time?

What were you like as a teenage? How did you experience life?

What was your first big step after high school?

The Story Timeline is adapted from our friends at The Noble Heart Ministries in Colorado Springs, CO.

THE STORY TIMELINE

ADULTHOOD (ages 20-present day)

Write down some thoughts, moments, experiences, emotions, people, and events from the time you were twenty till where you are right now. Depending on your age, it may be helpful to segment this time into specific decades. Because this time frame may be longer than the previous two, we've provided an extra page for writing notes. Here are some questions to help guide you on your way:

Who were some significant people in your life during that time? Were they helpful, or hurtful?

What events during this time, no matter how minor or major, had an effect on your life?

What did you learn from the people and circumstances in your life during this time?

What was your work situation like during this time?

Were you married during these years? Single? What has your relationship experience been like?

If you have kids, what has that experience been like for you?

The Story Timeline is adapted from our friends at The Noble Heart Ministries in Colorado Springs, CO.

THE STORY TIMELINE

The Story Timeline is adapted from our friends at The Noble Heart Ministries in Colorado Springs, CO.

APPENDIX

meet the guide team

When embarking on a journey, it is always good to have guides who have made the journey before. The Deepening Journey Guide Team have been on this road for years. They've made many mistakes, have fought many battles, and have won many victories. As they continue their own journeys of walking with God together, they are excited and honored to guide you on this incredible journey.

Robin Thompson

Robin is learning that it's okay to not be okay. To hold complexities. That there is room for far more than she ever thought, and that her voice is needed. She is learning how wise and good her body is, and that it can be trusted. Some of her sweetest moments with God are on her yoga mat, where body, soul, and spirit align so beautifully.

She believes she was made for sunshine and warm weather, the beach and really good coffee. Tacos and margaritas outdoors with friends make her come alive. She loves being home, adores the quiet, and loves laughing and traveling with her handsome husband, Michael. Time with their three grown daughters is especially treasured.

Mourning with those who mourn and rejoicing with those who rejoice is one of Robin's great passions.

Sherry Jennings

Sherry loves to travel and explore the world around her; yet in this season, she is discovering more and more the beauty of coming home to her own heart. Her favorite people are Scott, her husband of thirty years (give or take, they divorced and remarried each other), and their son Steven. Delighting in sunrises, camping, yoga, coffee with friends, playing in the dirt, and cultivating beauty around her, she is intrigued with the idea that she doesn't need to be in control of everything.

Gathering women, inviting them out of isolation and into friendship, and connecting them with other women thrills her heart - Sherry longs to see women becoming who they were created to be, experiencing the goodness of God, drawing their life and breath and way from Him, walking with Him together in flourishing.

Dana Andrechyn

Dana has loved being part of Zoweh's *Deepening Weekends* since 2012 and part of the greater Zoweh Team since 2016 as Zoweh's bookkeeper. Dana has been married for 35 years and counting to Jeff, and can be found most often these days on "The Adventure" in their Airstream Globetrotter with their West Highland White Terrier, Oscar, visiting family and friends and exploring the vast beauty found throughout the United States.

In recent years, writing poetry and musings have become a meaningful way to express the deep places of her heart on paper and to cultivate creativity. She also loves to set a table both literally and figuratively as a way to offer beauty, welcome, nourishment, and restoration to those who hunger and thirst with the hope that during the feasting, we would meet Jesus in our midst.

Lenné Hunt

Lenné brings a beautiful and deeply intimate way and strength to Zoweh and The Deepening Experience. Since adolescence, Lenné has lived with an awareness of Heaven's call to intimacy and relationship, and an equal awareness of what is pitted against that.

God has written deeply in her heart that words contain the power of life and death. Called to be a healer, much of Lenné's life has been spent journeying with people through the hard of their lives. In the spaces in between, her heart is fueled by creative endeavors, time in her garden, and the company of furry things.

the daily prayer

My dear Lord Jesus, I come to you now to be restored[1] in you – to renew my place in you, my allegiance to you, and to receive from you all the grace and mercy I so desperately need this day. I honor you as my sovereign Lord, and I surrender every aspect of my life totally and completely to you. I give you my body as a living sacrifice; I give you my heart, soul, mind and strength; and I give you my spirit as well. I cover myself with your blood[2] – my spirit, my soul, and my body. And I ask your Holy Spirit to restore my union with you, seal me in you, and guide me in this time of prayer.

Dear God, holy and victorious Trinity, you alone are worthy of all my worship, my heart's devotion, all my praise and all my trust and all the glory of my life. I worship you, bow to you, and give myself over to you in my heart's search for life. You alone are Life, and you have become my life. I renounce all other gods, all idols, and I give you the place in my heart and in my life that you truly deserve. I confess here and now that it is all about you, God, and not about me. You are the Hero of this story, and I belong to you. Forgive me, God, for my every sin. Search me and know me and reveal to me any aspect of my life that is not pleasing to you, and grant me the grace of a deep and true repentance.

Heavenly Father, thank you for loving me and choosing me before you made the world.[3] You are my true Father – my Creator, my Redeemer, my Sustainer, and the true end of all things, including my life. I love you, I trust you, I worship you. Thank you for proving your love for me by sending your only Son, Jesus, to be my substitute and representative.[4] I open up my life anew to all of his Life and all his work, which you ordained for me.[5] Thank you for including me in Christ,[6] for forgiving me my sins,[7] for granting me his righteousness,[8] for making me complete in him.[9] Thank you for making me alive with Christ,[10] raising me with him,[11] seating me with him at your right hand,[12] granting me his authority,[13] and anointing me with your Holy Spirit.[14] I receive it all with thanks and give it total claim to my life.

Jesus, thank you for coming for me, for ransoming me with your own life.[15] I honor you as my Lord, I love you, worship you, trust you. I embrace[16] you as my redemption, and I receive all the work and triumph of your Crucifixion, whereby I am cleansed from all my sin through your shed blood,[17] my old nature is removed,[18] my heart is circumcised unto God,[19] and every claim being made against me is disarmed.[20] I take my place in your cross and death, whereby I have died with you to sin and to my flesh,[21] to the world,[22] and to the evil one.[23] I take up my cross and crucify my flesh with all its pride, unbelief, and idolatry. I put off the old man.[24] I now bring the cross of Christ between me and all people, all spirits, and all things. Holy Spirit, apply to me the fullness of the work of the Crucifixion of Jesus Christ for me. I receive it with thanks and give it total claim to my life.

Jesus, I also embrace you as my new life,[25] my holiness and sanctification, and I receive all the work and triumph of your Resurrection, whereby I have been raised with you to a new life, to walk in newness of life, dead to sin and alive to God.[26] I am crucified with Christ and it is no longer I who live, but Christ who lives in me.[27] I now take my place in your Resurrection, whereby I have been made alive with you,[28] I reign in life through you.[29] I now put on the new man[30] in all holiness and humility, in all righteousness and purity and truth. Christ is now my life,[31] the one who strengthens me.[32] Holy Spirit, apply to me the fullness of the Resurrection of Jesus Christ for me. I receive it with thanks and give it total claim to my life.

Jesus, I also sincerely embrace you as my authority and rule, my everlasting victory over Satan and his kingdom, and I receive all the work and triumph of your Ascension, whereby Satan has been judged and cast down,[33] his rulers and authorities disarmed,[34] all authority in heaven and on earth given to you, Jesus,[35] and I have been given fullness in you, the head over all.[36] I take my place in your Ascension, whereby I have been raised with you to the right hand of the Father and established with you in all authority.[37] I bring your authority and your kingdom rule over my life, my family, my household, and my domain.

And now I bring the fullness of your work – your Cross, Resurrection, and Ascension – against Satan, against his kingdom, and against all his emissaries and all their work warring against me and my domain. Greater is he who is in me than he who is in the world.[38] Christ has given me authority to overcome all the power of the evil one and I claim that authority now over and against every enemy, and I banish them in the Name of Jesus Christ.[39] Holy Spirit, apply to me the fullness of the work of the Ascension of Jesus Christ for me. I receive it with thanks and give it total claim to my life. Holy Spirit, I sincerely embrace you as my Counselor, my Comforter, my Strength, and my Guide.[40] Thank you for sealing me in Christ.[41] I honor you as my Lord, and I ask you to lead me into all truth, to anoint me for all of my life and walk and calling, and to lead me deeper into Jesus today.[42] I fully open my life to you in every dimension and aspect – my body, my soul and my spirit – choosing to be filled with you, to walk in step with you in all things.[43] Apply to me, blessed Holy Spirit, all of the work and all of the gifts in Pentecost.[44] Fill me afresh, blessed Holy Spirit. I receive you with thanks and give you total claim to my life.

Heavenly Father, thank you for granting to me every spiritual blessing in the heavenlies in Christ Jesus.[45] I receive those blessings into my life today and I ask the Holy Spirit to bring all those blessings into my life this day. Thank you for the blood of Jesus. Wash me once more with his blood from every sin and stain and evil device. I put on your armor – the belt of truth, the breastplate of righteousness, the shoes of the readiness of the Gospel of peace, the helmet of salvation. I take up the shield of faith and the sword of the Spirit, the Word of God, and I wield these weapons against the evil one in the power of God. I choose to pray at all times in the Spirit, to be strong in you, Lord, and in your might.[46]

Father, thank you for your angels, may they guard me at all times this day.[47] Thank you for those who pray for me; I confess I need their prayers and I ask you to send forth your Spirit and rouse them, unite them, raising up the full canopy of prayer and intercession for me.[48]

I call forth the kingdom of the Lord Jesus Christ this day throughout my home, my family, my life and my domain. I pray all of this in the name of Jesus Christ, with all glory and honor and thanks to him.

Amen.

the daily prayer footnotes

1. There is a "daily-ness" to our walk with Christ, we have to choose to abide in Christ. It's not something that happens automatically, and we can lose connection with our head (Colossians 2:19). Not a loss of salvation, but a loss of that intimate connection to the Vine through which we receive his life. Every morning we bring our lives fully back to Christ and under his Lordship. It's important that we consecrate our whole being to Christ – our body (Romans 12:1), our soul (Luke 10:27) and our spirit (1 Corinthians 6:17).

2. 1 John 1:9

3. Ephesians 1:4

4. Romans 5:8

5. By entering into the work of Christ daily, we appropriate in a fresh way all he has already done for us. After all, Christ told us to take up our cross daily (Luke 9:23).

6. 1 Corinthians 1:30

7. Colossians 2:13

8. 2 Corinthians 5:21

9. Colossians 2:10

10. Colossians 2:13

11. Colossians 3:1

12. Ephesians 2:6

13. Luke 10:19, Ephesians 2:6

14. Ephesians 1:13

15. Matthew 20:28

16. By entering into the work of Christ daily, we appropriate in a fresh way all he has already done for us. After all, Christ told us to take up our cross daily (Luke 9:23).

17. 1 John 1:9

18. Colossians 2:11

19. Romans 2:29

20. Colossians 2:15

21. Romans 6:11

22. Galatians 6:14

23. Colossians 1:13

24. Ephesians 4:22

25. Having put off the old man, we are told to put on the new (Ephesians 4:24).

26. Romans 6:11

27. Galatians 2:20

28. Ephesians 2:5

29. Romans 5:17

30. Romans 6:4

31. Colossians 3:4

32. Philippians 4:13

33. John 12:31

34. Colossians 2:15

35. Matt 28:18

36. Colossians 2:10

37. Ephesians 2:6

38. 1 John 4:4

39. Luke 10:19

40. John 14:16, Acts 9:31

41. Ephesians 1:13

42. John 15:26, 16:13

43. Galatians 5:25

44. Ephesians 4:8

45. Ephesians 1:3

46. Ephesians 6:10-18

47. Hebrews 1:14

48. 2 Corinthians 1:8-11

movies we love

Encanto

Mulan (2020)

Little Women (2019)

The Hundred-Foot Journey

Tolkien

A Little Chaos

The Secret Life of Bees

Moana

Harriet

The Secret Garden (1993)

Wonder Woman

Mr. Holland's Opus

The Horse Whisperer

Inside Out

The Proposal

My Big Fat Greek Wedding

Hidden Figures

The Notebook

Jane Eyre

Titanic

Pride and Prejudice

About Time

Strictly Ballroom

Shall We Dance

Ever After

Mom's Night Out

Cinderella (2015)

Dance With Me

The Lord of the Rings trilogy

The Chronicles of Narnia series

The Young Victoria

Saving Mr. Banks

A Little Princess

50 First Dates

Stranger Than Fiction

Les Miserables

The Last of the Mohicans

Chocolat

Life as a House

Martian Child

The Blind Side

The Help

The Shack

Little

The Greatest Showman

Captain Marvel

War of the Worlds

The Kid

CODA

The purpose of a storyteller is not to tell you how to think, but to give you questions to think upon.

Brandon Sanderson

Zoweh does not necessarily endorse the entirety of R-rated films.

books we love

Begin Again *by Sharon Hersh*

The Sacred Romance *by Brent Curtis and John Eldredge*

Life of the Beloved *by Henri Nouwen*

The Healing Path *by Dan Allender*

To Be Told *by Dan Allender*

Healing the Wounded Heart *by Dan Allender*

Redeeming Heartache *by Cathy Loerzel and Dan Allender*

The Heart of a Warrior *by Michael Thompson*

Search and Rescue *by Michael Thompson*

The Gifts of Imperfection *by Brené Brown*

A Grace Disguised *by Jerry Sittser*

For more books we love that we didn't mention here, visit **zoweh.org/books-we-love.**

podcasts we love

Exploring More with Michael Thompson

Become Good Soil with Morgan Snyder

The Captivating Podcast

Being Known with Curt Thompson, MD

The Place we Find Ourselves, Adam Young

Wild at Heart Podcast, John Eldredge

The Bible Project

The Allender Center Podcast

also from zoweh

the
HEART OF A
WARRIOR
encounter

the
deepening
weekend

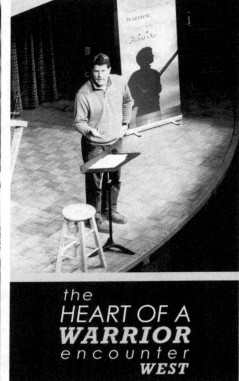

the
HEART OF A
WARRIOR
encounter
WEST

Learn more and register for upcoming events at **zoweh.org/events**

EXPLORING MORE
WITH MICHAEL THOMPSON

LISTEN

Listen on Apple Podcasts · GET IT ON Google Play · STITCHER · Spotify · SOUNDCLOUD · iHeart RADIO · YouTube   **zoweh.org/podcast**

Two people walking with God ... together.

CAN MARRIAGE REALLY BE FULFILLING?

INTIMACY

Through intentional and vulnerable conversation and sessions, couples will discover deeper intimacy in their marriage and with God.

STRENGTH

With biblical teaching, couples will explore the strength God created them with, and learn how to fight for each other, not against each other.

GLORY

By exploring each other's stories, couples will discover how God can partner with their unique marriage to offer his Kingdom life to the world.

zoweh.org/the-rendezvous-project

CPSIA information can be obtained
at www.ICGtesting.com
Printed in the USA
JSHW012106060722
27620JS00005B/14